Tin Pan Alley at the dawn of the century — not so much an actual place, more a way of business life. Publishers strategically near theatres, which are ever-hungry for hit songs. Harms were classy by Alley standards. Eccentric Fred Fischer may well have hurled his typewriter (in famous joke) through one of these very windows.
Wildcroft Pix

TIN PAN ALLEY

A PICTORIAL HISTORY (1919-1939)
WITH COMPLETE WORDS AND MUSIC OF FORTY SONGS

BY
IAN WHITCOMB

PADDINGTON PRESS
TWO CONTINENTS PUBLISHING GROUP
NEW YORK

WILDWOOD HOUSE
EMI MUSIC PUBLISHING
LONDON

First published 1975

Selection and text ©1975 by Ian Whitcomb

Songs © copyright for all territories
see details on individual songs
reproduced by arrangement with E.M.I. Music Publishing Ltd
and by courtesy of the copyright proprietors and licensees listed on p.251

American edition by Paddington Press Ltd,
Two Continents Publishing Group,
30 East 42nd Street,
New York City, New York 10017

Canadian edition by Paddington Press Ltd, distributed by
Random House of Canada,
370 Alliance Avenue, Toronto, Ontario

ISBN 0-8467-0041-7

Library of Congress Catalog Card No. 74-15920

English edition co-published
by Wildwood House Ltd, 1 Wardour Street, London W1V 3HE
and EMI Music Publishing Ltd,
138-40 Charing Cross Road, London WC2H OLD

ISBN 0 7045 0119 8

Design by John McConnell, Pentagram
Cover Illustration David Pearce

Ian Whitcomb's involvement with popular music extends back to the days when he collected sheet music for his school band. Since then his musical activities have been remarkably diverse. In 1965 (the year in which he took a History degree from Trinity College, Dublin) he wrote and recorded a hit song entitled "You Turn Me On." He spent three years meticulously researching a history of modern popular music, published in 1972 by Penguin, called *After the Ball*. *The New Yorker* magazine said that *After The Ball* is a "freewheeling, diverting history," and called the author a "brash, learned, funny, perspicacious" young man. Ian Whitcomb has produced a record, *Great Balls of Fire*, for Mae West. Mr. Whitcomb is a virtuoso ukulele player and an inexhaustible source of good songs, old and new.

Contents

A welcome
from Harry Warren

I've known Ian for several years and I can vouch that he's a fine historian as well as being a pretty good up-and-coming songwriter. He's a wonderful guy to delve into all this detail about us songwriters, because most of my working life people weren't interested in who wrote the songs they heard and sang and whistled. Fact is, I think they believed the screen stars made them up in the studio. Well, I guess that's OK because, after all, we weren't meant to be seen and heard in those days — unlike today's singer-songwriters. Still, it's nice to get a bit of recognition in a book.

I knew a lot of the twenties writers represented in Ian's book and especially admired Walter Donaldson. He was my model for years, but when I got going in the thirties he was on his ebb so we never got intimate socially. I did have the honor of writing with Ira Gershwin, but, you know, I never got to know him personally, I mean in his private life. We were craftsmen, we didn't analyze our work too much. We didn't have time. The guys were waiting on the set for the song before they could do anything, so we had to get the orders out fast. Al Dubin (I collaborated with him for years at Warner Brothers) and I were hardly ever given a good natural spot in a movie to place a song. The songs weren't written into the scripts much then. So we often had to dream them up out of clear air, and I would dig back to some melody I'd been knocking around in my subconscious for years. It's a self-taught business. You can learn harmony and arranging at a school, but you can't learn songwriting. Most of it's God-given, but then you have to work some.

I'm not a great man for words. I never wrote lyrics either. Piano music not chin music for me, but I'd just like to say that it gives me a warm feeling to see a book about these old writers — like somebody writing about the Middle Ages or the Wars of the Roses. Thanks!

Sincerely
Harry Warren

Certain of yet another hit, Al Jolson, Harry Warren and an accompanist run over a number from *Wonderbar* in confines of Warner Bros studios. *Harry Warren*

Who writes the words and music for all the girly shows? No one cares and no one knows . . . when they've got a lot of Dames! (From "Dames" by Al Dubin and Harry Warren).

Times change: the dancers and watchers become fans and the children of the fans become buffs — and here we are!

Busby Berkeley's lovelies form gigantic Ruby Keeler puzzle for Dick Powell's dream song "I Only Have Eyes For You" in *Dames* (Warner Bros, 1934). *Kobal Collection*

D-169

Introduction

This is a book of commercial music. I am honoring Tin Pan Alley, the world of the song-makers. The name "Tin Pan Alley" applied to the railroad flats around 28th and Broadway in New York City where the music publishing houses were clustered. Monroe Rosenfeld, a journalist, probably gave this area its name in a series of articles he wrote for *New York Herald*. The publishing houses were on top of each other, their windows wide open, tunes pouring out—the Babel reminded Rosenfeld of tin pans clanging.

It's a world that, unhappily, has vanished. Somewhere around the early sixties a notion started creeping into popular music that this joy-product could be fashioned into meaningful music, into Art. Misguided intellectuals charged into the Alley, all grim and grimy from the dark caves of Greenwich Village and dubious hinterland universities. Poor pop was called pap, or was analyzed into the ground — and was struck a blow from which it has never really recovered.

So this is a book about the old song salesmen, who wrote for mass consumption and whose successes created an industrial folk music. I've tried to stick to songs that aren't museum pieces but are decent musical works that sound good on the piano. There are one or two that were never hits but which make good social points, or deserve to have been hits and somehow were passed by. Sometimes I've been able to track down the story behind the song, but it would take forever to find out why the millions bought the songs. I mean, I personally like all the songs, but what chord was struck in the hearts of the masses that enticed them to spend hard-earned cash on, say "My Blue Heaven"? Was it the tune or the words? Or was it the way it was sung by Gene Austin?

The successful pop song is like a child that grows up, leaves the parent songwriter or writers, and marries the world. Then the world claims it as their number, which they got engaged to, which they sang all that summer holiday, which they danced to all night.

My heroes, the Alleymen, had their surest years in the first quarter of the century when the Song was the Thing. From the thirties on, technology (records, radios, talkies, electronics) tended to squash and smother the song. But even so, the electric monsters needed that song fuel. Without it — silence.

Today there are record freaks and dance band nuts. There are those who can tell you who's taking the hot cornet chorus on some old foxtrot 78. I have even met a man who specializes in British pop groups of 1963. But sheet-music shepherds are few.

Quite early in life I started amassing sheet music because I needed the words and the chords for the school band. When I saw the song in print I could really come to grips with it. Like stopping a film and looking at it frame by frame. Ah! *That's* what the chord is! I was score reading like they did at classical concerts, except this was pygmy compared with a concerto. But with a pop sheet I could eventually clamber on top of the effort and straddle it and use it. That's hard to do in High Art, which tends to overawe, towering and soaring heavenwards.

While I was at university I began analyzing, not content to be an audience. Had to why and wherefore the entertainment. History at college — finding the place of the King's Signet Ring in the development of medieval parliament — was fun but served little purpose. The historical technique applied to pop promised gold rewards. Perhaps the secret of the hit might be revealed. As I dug deeper in my researches I was taken back to the very beginning of pop music and the pop song. Around the 1890's I stopped, looked around and found myself in America, in New York, in an area called Tin Pan Alley.

Here a canny bunch of go-ahead buccaneer businessmen, filled with a zeal foreign to Europeans, and keenly aware of the new mass-market created by the American Industrial Revolution, decided to manufacture songs which might be bought by these unknown people. They fed theaters and parlors, cafés and dance halls with their wares. By 1910 The Alleymen had pushed hundreds of songs into million-selling sheets. These tall piano copies, fronted with shouting, colored art-work and spotted with ads for other songs, were the sole pop moneymakers until records, radio and talking pictures became the chief pop vehicles.

At first the owners of the new vehicles refused to pay the song owners any performance money. "We are honoring your work, we are giving you free publicity," they claimed. In 1914 the American Society of Composers, Authors and Publishers was formed to

DINNER GIVEN BY
THE AMERICAN SOCIETY OF COMPOSERS,
AUTHORS AND PUBLISHERS.
IN HONOR OF ITS PRESIDENT AND COUNSEL
MR. GEORGE MAXWELL
AND
MR. NATHAN BURKAN
LÜCHOWS. NOV. 27, 1914.
PHOTO BY
SCHLESINGER. NY.

I FOUND THIS PHOTOGRAPH IN MY TRUNK AND THOUGHT IT MIGHT BRING BACK SOME PLEASANT MEMORIES OF THOSE VISIONARY ZEALOTS WHO ATTENDED FIRST ASCAP DINNER

gather in the earnings, but at first the going was tough. Millions and millions of dollars were involved. Suits were fought, even bodyguards hired. But ASCAP gradually won its way and the money rolled in. By 1939 the society was a tight little club of established show- and Alley-writers (critics complained that hillbillies and bluesmen were excluded) sharing an annual cake of $4,300,000. ASCAP music, claimed the society, was America's music, and that was that. The broadcasters, unwilling to pay the increased rate that ASCAP intended charging in 1941, decided to form their own music-licensing society by tapping other sources such as writers who'd failed to make the ASCAP grade: hillbillies, boogie-woogie boys, lawyers, mechanics and even housewives. They called their society Broadcast Music Incorporated, and it was a success. The ASCAP grip on pop music was broken. The golden age of the well-turned standard was over. The barbarians were snarling at the gate. Which is reason enough to end our first collection of pop classics in 1939.

I've been talking about pop as an industry. But what about the music? Fortunately and curiously, just as the Alley began to wax fat, American music started limbering up and jerked to the surface of urban life at the end of the 1890's. The melting pot had produced a great stew of music: sounds from Ireland, Scotland, Russia, Serbo-Croatia and on and on. Jigs, reels, marches, polkas, waltzes — and mixed up in this swirl was the ex-African with an intriguing song and dance style soon to be called ragtime. Musically, it was non-stop syncopation driving along the old four-square harmonies and melodies. The lyrics were pepped up with slangy street phrases, lots of "ain'ts" and "honey babes", and this was a mighty change from the "thees" and "thous" of Victorian balladry. More spectacularly, these ragtime songs were accompanied by energetic love dances named after animals: turkey trot, bunny hug, kangaroo hop. It was all perfect for hustling, bustling twentieth-century America.

From being a song and dance associated with the rustic black man, ragtime by 1917 was the sound of the Yankee. Europeans, tired of their own popular music, eagerly accepted the friendly song invaders. The rag beat slid into the jazz beat as the various animal dances were gobbled up by the sleek fox-trot. From about 1917 pop songs hoping for hit status had to be danceable. The new dance bands, stripped down from the old large ball orchestras and substituting saxes for fiddles, were adept at reducing most songs to dance-floor fare.

All the time, however, that ragtime was the rage, the ballad, backbone of the business, was unbowed. Every year songs in waltz-time (and even no-time), about timeless love set to old oak tunes sold in the millions — "My Gal Sal" (1905), "Down By The Old Mill Stream" (1910), "M-O-T-H-E-R, A Word That Means The World To Me" (1915), "Till We Meet Again" (1918).

I've boiled the pop story down to a simple truth: man cannot live by beat alone, he needs the dream. Even today nostalgic yearning jostles next to instant sex on the hit charts — "Tie A Yellow Ribbon Round The Old Oak Tree" (Dawn) and "Here I Am — Come And Take Me" (Al Green).

Lastly, Tin Pan Alley was shot into streamlining its sales techniques and output capabilities by the coming of the Great War to America. Songwriters filled the breach (encouraged by President Wilson) with excellent war propaganda songs ("Just Like Washington Crossed The Delaware General Pershing Will Cross The Rhine") covering every aspect of the war ("There'll be A Hot Time For The Old Men When The Young Men Go To War" — this went too far and was banned). Officially the songs were spread by the Army song leaders, but vaudeville showed the flag nightly, Caruso cut "Over There" and British Tommies were heard to sing the same song — with special emphasis on the line that ran "The Yanks are coming".

By the war's end popular music was American music.

After the war

I'm cheating slightly by beginning with "I'm Always Chasing Rainbows". This reflective ballad with the mellifluous title was first heard in spring 1918, when guns were still pounding the Western Front — but I couldn't resist snatching one of my favorites from out of the war period. And besides, the song's proof that, though 1918 was crammed with shoot-'em-up war efforts, there was still room for a philosophical number.

"Rainbows" has nothing about guns and drums, but it harps, with perhaps a sprinkling of self-pity, on personal failure. We all suffer from that, so a healthy wallow isn't a bad thing. Joe McCarthy, the author, gives no details of the disasters — stock market crashes? The sack? Wife trouble? — so we can all identify. That's a good rule of thumb for a lasting pop hit: don't be too specific. Don't give us the room number of her chalet or what you had for breakfast — of course, a girl's name is O.K. as we'll see later with "Charmaine" and "Chloe". Sound, sound, sound — very important. At that time "lulling" was very often the order of the day.

Now what about the philosophy in the song? Actually, I doubt whether the public paid much attention to the argument. Rather they — like me — were wafted along by the stream of dreams, schemes and clouds drifting by. It's a sinuous melody and a strong one. So strong that the arranger has placed it in the left hand and given the right hand bird-chords and decorative fills with a quasi-classical chromatic run at the very end of the chorus (I shall try not to get carried away technically too often). We ought just to note how excellent this arrangement is, how very *pianistic* it is. This sheet sold a million, so there must have been at least that many competent pianists around. And *this* was the pop public! As we dart through the years we'll see the piano parts get simpler with less fiddly fills and we could conclude, "Ah! The masses are getting lazier and less literate and more passive." On the other hand, it might be that people were keener to improvise on their guitars or ukes or saxes and didn't need these involved corny accompaniments. Look at today's average sheet pop and you'll see a stripped-down arrangement: melody, chord symbol and bass root note.

"Rainbows" caused a bit of a stir in classical circles because its fetching melody had been fetched by vaudeville pianist Harry ("By The Beautiful Sea") Carroll from Chopin's "Fantasie Impromptu In C Sharp Minor".* I don't see much wrong with that when viewed from the pop market-place. If McCarthy and Carroll were striving to be artists for art's sake — in search of that wretched perversity called "originality" — then we might be justified in labeling

Home from the Great War, U.S. servicemen and sweethearts parade down a New York avenue in 1918. Goodbye war songs, Hello Jazz!

them "copycats". But good pop is crazy quilt patchwork from any and all sources (providing they're not in copyright), and Chopin, like "Auld Lang Syne", was in the public domain, a part of the folk fund.

Harry Fox created "Rainbows" in the musical comedy *Oh Look!* and gave the show its only hit, but such a socko one that the show was saved. This was a recurring story on Broadway and the bane of those artists in light music struggling to make American musical comedy into more than a show case for songs. Jerome Kern, for example, said that "Songs must be suited to the action and mood of the play," and that his mission was to "do something for the future of American music, which today has no class whatsoever."

But the public seemed to prefer a few rattling good tunes and a fairy tale. In 1919 they flocked to see *Irene*, in which pulse-trembler Edith Day played a poor shopgirl whisked into High Society with subsequent riches and everlasting love. Cinderella stories captivated Broadway for the next few years, and even poor Kern found himself writing hits for one called *Sally*.

---

*The stir was still on even in the late twenties: Harry O. Osgood in *So This Is Jazz* " wrote that "Mr Carroll's own additions to the melody of Chopin joined smoothly on to the original tune; there is no disturbance of line. And the ultimate result was that thousands of people who love music heard a beautiful tune which would ever have been a stranger to them . . . Thus the multitude came to know that Chopin, instead of being a classicist to be shied at, wrote catchy, whistly tunes; that he was one who might be investigated without fear of ennui the next time a recital-playing pianist came along". Isaac Goldberg, the first to appreciate American pop music and to research its history, countered with: "When Carroll took the Chopin melody (to the people) he denatured it. He deprived it of its accompaniment, thus at once altering its mood; he wrenched it from its context; in a single strong word, he fouled it".

Irene's standout number was "Alice Blue Gown". In fact the show was often referred to by theatergoers as "The Alice Blue Gown Show". The number is a lilting waltz, with a see-saw chorus start of pleasing intervals, and an overall charm of china tea-set primness. The " lyrics" (show-tune wordsmen liked to use this euphemism) are by the "Rainbows" man* and Alice Blue was a shade of blue of which Alice Roosevelt, Teddy's daughter, was fond.

While the musical was in the talk-stage, songwriters McCarthy and Tierney asked star Edith Day to name her favorite song. Her choice was "Little Grey Home In The West", an English hit ballad of 1911 by Wilmot and Lohr. At once the boys knuckled down and knocked "Alice" into the same shape as "Grey Home". That's a clue to writing commercial music: fashion the song around a previous hit, using the model as a take-off pad. Chances are you'll finish up with something just different enough to be choice but not avant-garde.

Broadway musicals were to provide the cream of the class songs, but the Alley continued to turn out rollicking tabloids about street life as currently lived, with an edge of comedy (I always think that certain edge is important to pop). Lewis, Young and Donaldson's 1919 smash† "How Ya Gonna Keep 'Em Down On The Farm?" was permissible as hit material in spite of the taboo subject of war, because the song posed a social question plaguing economists and quite a few of the people. Anyway, within the Alley tradition of "answer" and "follow-up" songs it was fine. Antecedents would include "Good Bye Broadway, Hello France!", "Over There" and "Good Bye Ma! Good Bye Pa! Good Bye Mule!".)

The countryside was emptying and the cities were filling up. Citybillies traditionally roared at the antics of rustic "rubes" (Reubens) and vaudevillians were always armed with a few jeers at the sticks hicks. New Yorker Irving Berlin had his cake and ate it in 1914 when he pictured Farmer Brown raising the dickens in a cabaret far from cows and chickens ("This Is The Life" he told his wife). Next minute we have Berlin writing "Gee! How I Wish Again That I Was In Michigan Down On The Farm". So there was a back-to-nature yearn even then! Our "How Ya Gonna Keep 'Em" composer, Walter Donaldson, had put in a 1915 rube refrain with "You'd Never Know That Old Home Town Of Mine"— because the hicks were night-clubbing and car-riding.

"Farm" is at the end of the vaudeville ragtime line. Its two-four jig-march beat, so ubiquitous for twenty years, so representative of the bucolic spring in the American new century spirit, was gradually giving way to the sludgier four-four of the fox-trot, which was to reign supreme at least until the next world war. The "Till ready" repeat vamp just before the verse starts was practical in vaudeville days: a useful phrase for the pit orchestra to play until the act was ready to begin — for often the singer liked to squeeze every ounce of preliminary applause, or maybe he was finishing a drop of backstage tipple. The verse is quite long (we shall see these story set-ups gradually disappear as pop gets less theatrical) and the chorus uses the brand-new catch-verb "to jazz", meaning to muck about in a possibly amorous manner. Jazz wasn't only a new music, then. At the end of the chorus we have a joke passage ("Imagine Reuben when he meets his pa, He'll kiss his cheek and holler 'oo-la-la'"), followed by a repeat of the title, probably intended to cover the gales of laughter with a flash-thunder finish and a stunning exit into the wings for a well-earned drink. Sophie Tucker and (separately) Eddie Cantor popularized this song, though dozens of acts featured it. Acts weren't necessarily associated with one particular song, except in the golden years of the British music hall (around 1880-1920) when stars guarded their songs jealously. Alley pop became public property, and stayed that way until the rock record artists appeared in the mid-fifties.

---

*Lyricist Joe McCarthy was straightening his tie in theaterland — he'd recently penned such vaude ribaldries as "What Do You Want To Make Those Eyes At Me For?" and "They Go Wild, Simply Wild, Over Me".
†From now on the reader must assume that all the songs are smashes unless I say otherwise.

HERBERT BRENON PRESENTS THE **FALL OF THE ROMANOFFS**

WILLIAM FOX PRESENTS **THEDA BARA** AS **CLEOPATRA** THE VAMPIRE OF THE NILE DIRECTION OF J. GORDON EDWARDS **LYRIC THEATRE NOW**

Vaudeville's days as King Pleasure are already numbered. Movies are to be the mass entertainment in 1920s and 1930s. Tin Pan Alley noted success of this 1916 epic movie by including vamp Theda Bara and studio veep William Fox in lyrics of "At The Moving Picture Ball". *Wildcroft Pix*

Eddie Cantor
with the
Midnight Rounders

Featured by
Lou Holtz and George White's
Scandals of 1920

Gus Van and Schenck Joe
with
Ziegfeld's Follies

Introduced by Al Jolson
in
Sinbad

Jack Strouse
Century Promenade
Atop The
Century Theatre
New York City

Arthur West
with
Fanchon Marco Satires

Ted Lewis
Greenwich Follies

A round-up of songmakers. Alleymen knew that without these performer-pluggers (vaudevillians, bandsmen, recording artists, radio singers (revuesicians) they were but unsung Miltons. Jolson was the greatest song salesman of them all. *Wildcroft Pix*

Walter Donaldson's "My Buddy" (with Gus Kahn words) is often thought of as a war song but in fact it dates from 1922. I suppose the buddy could be a dead comrade missed by the hero (next year the war lament "That Old Gang Of Mine" topped the sales lists) but equally the buddy could be a girl-friend — best gals were often real pals at that time.

The tune's wistful pine rests a lot on stretched diminished chords as it rocks in waltz-time back and forth on two notes a third apart. Donaldson came upon this nifty musical catch-phrase quite by accident . . . .

One evening he was at Gus Kahn's place trying to hammer out hits on the home piano while Kahn paced the room drumming up words. Da-da! Da-da! Da-da! kept interrupting them from the nursery. The wordsman investigated and discovered that the noise was being made by his baby son on a two-note toy instrument. "I'll stop him, Walt. Don't worry", promised Kahn. "No, wait, Gus", as Donaldson doodled the same toy phrase on the piano. "I think we got something here". And "My Buddy" came to life, closely followed by "Carolina In The Morning". Or it may have been the other way around. Anyway—two hits in one night!

This same musical phrase (a trick or device in lesser hands) is the very basis of

Sophie Tucker may look dreamy here but she could belt a number better than the lustiest. She'd pushed "Some of These Days" into a million seller and in 1919 she helped "How Ya Gonna Keep 'Em Down On The Farm?" into the smash realm. Californian Harry Fox, revuesician and cabaret artist, was allegedly the inventor of the fox-trot. True or false, he caused a storm with his nutty-sad rendition of "I'm Always Chasing Rainbows" in *Oh Look! Wildcroft Pix*

Richard Whiting's "Japanese Sandman", a 1920 descriptive escape popularized by the stalwart boomer Norah Bayes in vaudeville, and by Paul Whiteman and his band in a very clever arrangement on record. This tune, though ultra-simple like most of Whiting's work, has really excellent harmony and this from a man who never had a music lesson in his life. Apparently he feared that instruction might ruin his natural ability.

The open fifths of the tune harmony suggest dainty little oriental ladies bouncing about, yet the choppy tune certainly has a ragtime flavor. In the verse there are some rich changes on the minor theme, a touch of syncopation quite suddenly, and major flashes anticipating the shift into the key of F major. Now, though the Whiteman arrangement is clever, it's a dance record and much of the harmonic subtlety is omitted. In a re-creation recording session of his old hits made in the late forties, Whiteman torpedoed "Sandman". Tossed it away in a slap-happy good-time jazz version. The dance band master had camped on himself!

The words, by ex-bank clerk Raymond Egan, invite us on a magic carpet trip to a land of mystery where we spy on a Japanese mother and meet an Aladdin — a very today person, who rather mystically promises improved tomorrows. "Then you'll be a bit older in the dawn when you wake and you'll be a bit bolder with the new day you make" — this has a Dale Carnegie touch about it. Of course, during World War II "Sandman" royalties dried up, but afterwards they rolled in again and today the song's an all-time standard. You can hear it in U.S. dentist waiting-rooms.

Oriental-type songs had enjoyed popularity for a few years before this Whiting-Egan song. In 1915 "Siam" and "Bom-Bombay" had been visited and next year Rudolf Friml took us on "Allah's Holiday". And there was "Hindustan", a wow of a one-step, and the inspiration for "Swanee", as we shall see later. In 1919 or so, a ragtime pianist called Johnny Black "borrowed" an intriguing melody off a vaudevillian called Felix Bernard, and, with some Eastern bits, offered it to publisher Fred Fisher as a ragtime instrumental entitled "Turkish Tom Tom". Fisher wrote a slight story to the tune, about a stranger (is he a traveling salesman, an Armenian carpet dealer, American tourist, even a remaindered British Officer?)— stealing easily from the Sultan's clutches a maid called "Dardanella". Now, one of the hooks of this song was a murmuring boogie-ish bass line and this became the cause of a plagiarism suit brought by Fisher — a hell of a character, so they say, and always good for a joke or two — against the rather regal theater composer Jerome Kern. Kern's "Ka-Lu-A", claimed Fisher, was a steal from "Dardanella" — listen to that bass pattern.

This was a real kick in the imperious behind for Kern. Such distinguished musicians as Leopold Stokowski and Victor Herbert were called on by Kern to vouch that this murmuring bass trick had been used by nineteenth-century music masters. Had the theater man been a little less sour in court he might have won, but the jury awarded a token sum to our Alleyman.

Throughout pop history there have been cases of plagiarism. Proof is very difficult — you've got to show how the thief deliberately set out to steal — and it's not simply a matter of a certain number of bars. In the case of "In A Little Spanish Town" versus "Why", composer Anthony Newley simply denied ever having heard the song he was accused of stealing from. But Jerry Herman lost substantial royalties from his "Hello Dolly" to the owners of the earlier "You're My Sunflower". Well, of course, pop shouldn't be concerned with originality, as I've said before, but with the newly familiar. Nostalgic novelty.

Round about the early twenties dance bands began to sprout in the thousands. Many used stock arrangements, but the ideal was to give the outfit a distinctive sound through such natty arrangements as Paul Whiteman's. Both "Japanese Sandman" and "Dardanella" were million-selling records. As a result piano sheet copy arrangements went into a decline.

2

I'm Always Chasing Rainbows

Lyrics by
JOSEPH McCARTHY

Music by
HARRY CARROLL

race, just a wild goose chase, And my dreams have all been de-

nied. _____ Why have I al ways been a

fail - ure, What can the rea - son be? I

rall. *dim.*

won-der if the world's to blame, I won-der if it could be me?

rall. *dim.*

5

sun-shine, I al-ways look and find the rain, Some fel-lows make a winning

some-time, I nev-er ev-en make a gain, Be-lieve me, I'm

al-ways chas-ing rain - - bows! Wait-ing to find a lit-tle

blue bird in vain. vain.

I'm Alway Chasing Rainbows 4

ALICE BLUE GOWN

from the musical comedy

Irene

MARION THOMAS

CHICAGO, ILL.

James Montgomery

music by
HARRY TIERNEY
lyrics by
JOSEPH McCARTHY
staged by
EDWARD ROYCE

60

ALICE BLUE GOWN

Words by
JOSEPH McCARTHY

Tune Ukulele

Music by
HARRY TIERNEY

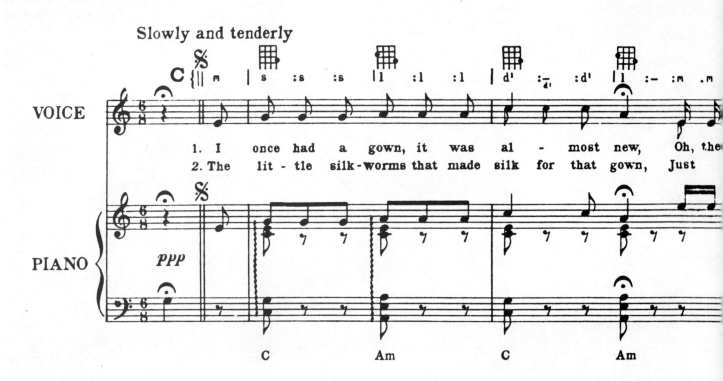

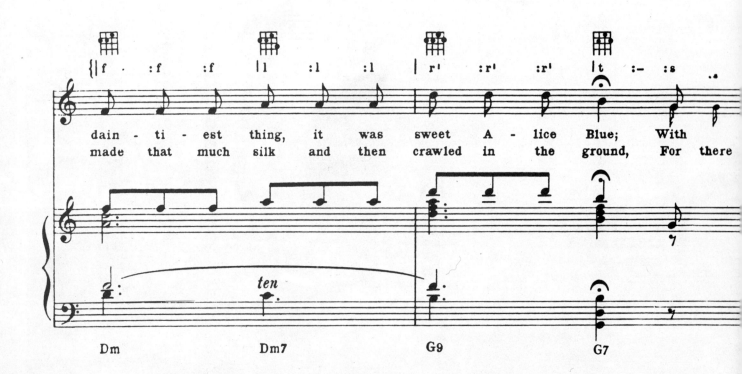

The letters below Bass Stave indicate names of Chords for Piano Accordion & Guitar

Copyright 1920, by Leo Feist, Inc., Feist Building, New York   F.& D.Ltd. 1668

FRANCIS, DAY & HUNTER, Ltd. 138-140, Charing Cross Road, London.W.C.2.

F.& D.Ltd 16684

How 'ya gonna keep 'em down on the farm?

(After they've seen Paree.)

Words by
SAM M. LEWIS & JOE YOUNG.

Music by.
WALTER DONALDSON.

"Reu-ben, Reu-ben, I've been think-ing," Said his wif - ey dear;......
"Reu-ben, Reu-ben, You're mis - tak-en"; Said his wif - ey . dear;......

"Now that all is peace-ful and calm, The boy will soon be back on the farm";
"Once a farm-er, al-ways a jay,.... And farm-ers al - ways stick to the hay";.

Mis - ter Reu-ben start-ed wink-ing, And slow - ly rubbed his chin;.............. He
"Moth - er Reu-ben, I'm not fak - in', Tho' you may think it strange;......... But

pulled his chair up close to moth - er, And he asked her with a grin;"..............
wine and wom-en play the mis - chief With a boy who's loose with change";.........

London, England: B. FELDMAN & Cº, Ltd.

CHORUS.

How 'ya gon-na keep 'em down on the farm, Af-ter they've seen Pa - ree?......

How 'ya gon-na keep 'em from Picc - a - dil - ly, Jazz-in' a-'roun',..... And paint-in' the town?

How 'ya gon-na keep 'em a - way from harm? That's a mys-ter - y;...... They'll ne-ver
Im-ag-ine

want to see a rake or plow,.... And who the deuce can par-ley-vous a cow?.... How 'ya gon-na
Reu-ben when he meets his pa,...... He'll kiss his cheek and hol-ler "oo-la - la'!.....

1.
keep 'em down on the farm, After they've seen Pa - ree?......
2.
-ree?.........

D.S

How 'ya gonna keep 'em down on the fa m?

MY BUDDY
SONG

Lyric by
GUS KAHN

Music by
WALTER DONALDSON

REFRAIN Valse Moderato

My Buddy-3

THE JAPANESE SANDMAN.

Words by
RAYMOND B. EGAN.

Music by
RICHARD A. WHITING.

Copyright 1920 by Jerome H. Remick & Cº, New York & Detroit.

London, England: B. FELDMAN & CO., LTD.

The Japanese Sandman.

8

4

REFRAIN.

The Japanese Sandman.

The Japanese Sandman.

DARDANELLA

Words by
FRED FISHER

Tune
Ukulele

Music by
FELIX BERNARD and
JOHNNY S. BLACK

The letters below Bass Stave indicate names of Chords for Piano Accordion & Guitar

Copyright 1919, by McCarthy & Fisher, Inc. New York

F & D Ltd 15370.

3

re - nian. _____ Soon I shall re-turn to Turk-e - stan, _____
bear him. _____ So be - neath the O-ri-en-tal moon,

_____ I will ask for her heart and hand. _____
_____ I'll be woo-ing my love real soon.

CHORUS

Oh _____ sweet Dar-da-nel-la, I love your harem eyes. I'm _____ a luck-y fel-low

to capture such a prize. Oh, Al-lah knows my love for you _____ And he tells you to be true, _____ Dar-da-

F. & D. Ltd. 15370.

Printed in England by WEST CENTRAL PRINTING CO. LTD. London.

F & D Ltd 15370.

Jazz age

Nobody really knows the origins of the word "jazz". Modern research tells us breathlessly that it was first seen at the turn of the century in a San Francisco newspaper. Certainly the word was in black-ghetto use in the 1890's: to jazz was to copulate. Ragtime veteran Eubie Blake told me this — with a blush, because he's a man of dignity who dresses smartly and is not overkeen on that "jungle" rhythm. Sure, blacks jazzed and rocked and rolled and balled the jack — didn't everybody? Why the fuss?

The fuss was whipped up by the whites who seemed to be besotted with the beat. All through this century they've shaken their bodies in mad abandon to syncopated music and attempted to live the way they imagined the blacks to live: loose dresses, loose morals, forbidden drugs, and so on. Today they sport pre-torn denim overalls. And all the while the blacks were getting up in the world, saving for silk threads, for dash, class. *Elegance*. Thus a quite extraordinary coming and going in social history: whites sliding down the pit, blacks reaching up for the stars. Popular music has reflected this trend from rag to rock . . . .

In Tin Pan Alley, 1918, the cry went up: "Find out what this jazz is all about! But if you can't — serve up the mixture as before with a new label!"

Will Von Epps, Alleyman, wrote a note to his men: "It seems to me, boys, that this jazz is played by a band all tooting different tunes in a kind of race to see who can finish first. Generally it's a dead heat. But go see the Original Dixieland Jazz Band, fellows, if you don't believe me".

This five-piece outfit from New Orleans had stunned New York. Pretty soon vaudevillians, publishers and arrangers had worked out roughly what it was all about. Pens scratched manuscript paper; bandleaders took note of the hot burns of the cornet player and the trombonist's smears. Jazz was absorbed by the new and swelling danceband business. Soon: dance band = big business.

By the mid-twenties every city and every town and even the golf clubs had dance bands in four-four time. It was the age of the dance band, and though they could cut some hot stuff they could get with the smoochy numbers too. Paul Whiteman was ace at this — his repertoire ranged from Beethoven to Berlin.

At college the swiftest way to become a big cheese was to get into a dance band. As student J.D. Spalding II wrote in an issue of *Kollege Kapers*: "It's applesauce to say that football is the bee's knees this season. Every cake-eater knows that the way to land a flapper is

to stroke the skins, badger the banjo, squeeze the sax, tease the trumpet. And if you're keen for a neck session in a jalopy, whip out your uke!"

The ukulele meant "little flea" to the Hawaiians. They'd adopted the mini-guitar off Portuguese sailors years back. Round about 1915 America went crazy for Hawaiian bands with their ukes and steel guitars. A plethora of these bands toured vaudeville and established the two novelty instruments. Ukuleles had but four strings, were very portable (for canoes, punts and parties) and gave off a pleasingly mellow chunk-chunk. Piano sales dropped. Publishers started reducing their songs to ukulele chord diagrams. Even Wagner could be analyzed in terms of C dominant seventh (with uke capo on first fret). May Singhi Breen was in great demand as a uke chord provider on pop sheets, while Roy Smeck was considered a wizard in performance. He could actually play tunes, not just strum.

Ukulele Ike (real name Cliff Edwards) wowed with his nifty strumming rolls and his superb moaning. He was but one of a new breed of singers called "crooners", who bobbed up around the mid-twenties, some peppy, some smoochy, but all unlike the earlier legitimate song—belters. The old boys tended to roll their R's and enunciate like mad. They took no liberties with their texts. The new set made love to the microphone (a new creature in pop) or howled under the moon up pet-creek in a canoe without a paddle.

Tops among the early crooners were "Whispering" Jack Smith, Gene Austin and Art Gillham (The Whispering Pianist). By the end of the twenties they had been eclipsed by the dapper Rudy Vallee, and he, in turn, by Bing Crosby, who clinched the style and became the model for all subsequent popular singers until the fifties.

Jack Smith strolled at a talk, occasionally soaring in actual melody. A whisky-smooth voice with beautiful enunciation, unlike many of his crooner brethren. His whisper

Ukulele Ike (real name: Cliff Edwards), brilliant strummer and blue moaner who started recording in 1919, leads chorus of M.G.M's *Hollywood Revue of 1929*. He later scored as voice of Jiminy Cricket in *Pinocchio*, died alone and bankrupt in Hollwyood, 1972. *Kobal Collection*

volume was the result of his involvement in a gas attack in World War I while he was serving Uncle Sam as a doughboy. He was successful in cabaret in the early twenties and was billed as "The Friendly Song Delineator". How on earth he was heard above the band in those pre-mike days (before 1924) I shall never know. He was a natural for electrical recording when it appeared in 1924 and had a slew of hits with Victor records. He toured England and Germany, recording in both countries, and on his return to New York he settled down to radio station work and then obscurity. In May 1951, he was so thrilled by a television baseball game that he had a massive heart attack and died.

During his peak years he had the honor of inspiring such singers as "Whispering" Billy Day, Confidential Charlie, and "Whispering" Bobby Gray, an ex-drawing room balladeer slumming. But Gene Austin put Smith's record sales in the shade with his version of "My Blue Heaven", the first million-selling vocal record. Austin, unlike Smith, had a high lilting tenor with not a little blues. He loved to fool with the tune, coming up with some plaintive prairie howls. From Shreveport, Louisiana, he had real country roots and he'd toured with the circus, too. After he became a hit singer he met up with hillbilly hero Jimmie Rodgers, the singing Brakeman, and liked to entertain the ailing blues yodeller on his palatial yacht. And he leaned towards jazz — went out of his way to use Fats Waller on record sessions, when others protested that the roly pianist indulged too much in the sauce.

Art Gillham (the Whispering Pianist) is a man I love on record. Thanks to Brian Rust's fascinating *Complete Entertainment Discography*,* I now know that Art Gillham came from St Louis, Missouri, fought for the U.S. Army in World War I, was a pioneer broadcaster, made a lot of records for Columbia, and retired in 1937 to become head of a business college in Atlanta, Georgia.

This triumvirate of pioneer crooners came to fame through electrification. Only the microphone and electric recording could pick up their love murmurs (unless you were being wooed close-to by one of the chanters) and these were established by the mid-twenties. Over the radio airwaves the crooners thrilled feminine hearts from farm to mansion; on thick shellac 78's they provided songs of solace and rhythms of rest, making for a peace that passed understanding.

Dance bands and crooners made up the bulk of record production in the twenties. Sales zoomed until the Depression, when they plummeted, but by 1939 there were million-sellers again. By that time we are on the eve of the disc jockey and that's another story.

Radio stations and record companies needed product. Lots more than usual — they gobbled up songs at an enormous rate and spat out hits which withered and died in only weeks. This terrified the Alley publishers but they plugged on. And in their sometimes oblique manner the pop writers turned out musical social history and some nifty tunes as well.

In "Stumbling" (1922) a poor devil describes his trouble with two left feet while trying to negotiate the new dances. Basically these were variations on the animal dances developed during the ragtime era. His girl, a typical trendy flapper, could step like a fox quite naturally even with her stockings rolled low and her corset off. These ladies were clearly taking command and bossing the men, leading them from purple dance hall to white cottage and domesticity.

The lead line of the chorus has an exhilarating syncopation, a hammering off-the-beat repetition (the hook phrase which probably made it a hit). Writer Zez Confrey had cut his teeth making dizzy piano rolls for the QRS company and was such a dazzling pianist and rhythm salesman that Henry Osgood included him in his book *So This Is Jazz*, and Paul Whiteman had him perform at his 1924 concert of Symphonic Jazz.

The Complete Entertainment Discography by Brian Rust with Allen G. Debus (Arlington House, New Rochelle, 1973).

As couple listen in to early radio, announcer at WJZ, New York (owned by Westinghouse) readies them for piano recital. Drawing-room props and drapes were there to help quell performer nervousness as well as unwanted sound. *Milt Larsen, Bettman Archive.*

    "Ain't We Got Fun" (1921) would seem to be the slogan of the roaring twenties, but on close examination of the words it turns out to be observations made by the next-door neighbour of poverty-stricken newlyweds. They look on the bright side. In fact, America was going through a period of postwar depression before the lush years so the song echoed a general feeling. However, the hit record by the Benson Orchestra of Chicago was without vocal refrain, purely a dance record. In the early twenties most hit records were instrumentals because people were buying for dancing only. The tune would be plugged relentlessly for three minutes or so, the band adding frilly ornamentation — cunning sax breaks and stop choruses. The arranger was rising. The catch phrase is *Boing!* — Every morning, *Boing!* — Every evening, *Boing!* Ain't we got fun! — the *boing* on the first beat being the catcher. But, curiously, composer Richard Whiting* wrote the tune originally without the *boing* so that "Every morning" came in on the first beat. However, the bands re-phrased it and coaxed the song into a smash. Whiting wised up in his following song, making sure he used both the *boing* anticipation trick and the Chinesey open fifths of "Japanese Sandman".

* Known in the trade as The Reverend, but a fine party-giver who owned and operated his own home brewery.

The result, "Bimini Bay" (1921) is stunningly clever, full of weird hovering harmonies in the verse (see bars three and four) and dashing syncopations in the chorus. The story takes a dig at Prohibition (fairly recently enforced) telling of a topical tropical island where the booze flows freely. Gus Kahn and Ray Egan touched on a subject close to the hearts of a multitude of songwriters. So many of them had love affairs with the bottle. Though the song was recorded by a wealth of bands it never caught on like "Ain't We Got Fun", and the boys went sadly back to the drawing board.

Built to rival Italian namesake, Venice, California, was developed from culture oasis into fun and sun land. By the 1920s you could hardly hear the surf for strumming of ukes, crying of fun-fair barkers, grinding of movie cameras, clinking of ice in illicit hootch, and clunking of oil wells. *Insurance & Trust Company of Los Angeles.*

America has enjoyed a hang-up about the Old South since the days of Stephen Foster and his plantation songs like "Way Down Upon The Swanee River". In the 1970's pop music still imagines that the real gritty, funky stuff comes from steaming southern swamps. The noble savage stalks even still — although your flesh-and-blood urban black may yearn for a white Mercedes. I recall a leather-jacketed BBC pop-music producer explaining to me why it was impossible that I, as a singer, could produce soulful, meaningful pop: "You see, the trouble is you've not *suffered* like a real southern black has suffered . . . like the other half now? With ice?"

Dixieland, where laughing belles and watermelon grinners cavorted at the Greek-pillared mansion, featured greatly in the late teens and early twenties songs: "They Made It Twice As Nice As Paradise And They Called It Dixieland", "Carolina In The Morning", "Everything Is Peaches Down In Georgia". The actual hillbillies themselves liked to sing these romantic concoctions, while the cotton failed and the cabin collapsed. Now, I love the South and spend a good deal of time there but it isn't like these songs, which are more like never-never land. And I'm sure it's the mellifluous ring of the names — Kentucky, Carolina, Tennessee — which helped sell the style. Piddletrenthide* doesn't seem to have that same ring.

"Carolina in the Morning" (1922) is a superior example of the Dixie genre, mainly because of its catchy words with their edge of humor. This, of course, is the tune inspired by Gus Kahn's son and his musical toy (see, "My Buddy"). Strike up a chorus of "Carolina" in any British pub and you'll be joined by the customers.

"Dapper Dan" is the super-lovin' man strutting around below the Mason-Dixon line, his pals being "Red Hot Henry Brown" and "Lovin' Sam — The Sheik of Alabam". (Incidentally, "Sheik" became the trade name for a rubber contraceptive popular in America.) These "hot coons", which the urban imagination invested with prodigious sexual abilities, not to mention athleticism — were the children of the "coon song" heroes of the late 1890's — for example in "Pump Away Joseph" and "Red Hot Member". In the Jazz Age they swung away in harness with the dusky Arab-Valentino types ("The Sheik of Araby") and were big in Britain too, where Jack Buchanan, gangly clubman in topper, made a fiery record of "Dapper Dan", ably accompanied by the Trix Sisters. Albert Von Tilzer (born Gumm) provides a stubby little melody with a sprinkling of blue notes and plunk-plunk on-the-beat chords in the bass. A decent sample of Alley jazz.

It's interesting that "Ain't We Got Fun", with a philosophy that money isn't everything, was a hit while "Any Place Where I Make Money Is Home Sweet Home To Me" (1923) was a dog. Too ahead of its time, perhaps — though the song's message is spot on. Business was starting to boom. Everyman and his wife were soon playing the Stock Exchange. Deals not ideals. Even the president's men had their fingers in the till. Adman Bruce Barton blessed Big Business by writing a best seller in which he named Jesus Christ as the founder of it all. And business boosters had their very own prayer which ended, "I thank Thee for the joy of battle in the business arena, the thrill of victory and the courage to take defeat like a good sport! I thank Thee for children, friendships, books, fishing, the game of golf, my pipe — and the open fire in a chilly evening. Amen."

Curiously, the cult of business coincided with the moral cleanliness movement, which had had its greatest victory in the Prohibition Act. The *Ladies' Home Journal* demanded that "Unspeakable Jazz Must Go", and by the end of the decade very little hot jazz was heard on the radio. Networks introduced tight censorship. Such novelties as "How Could Red Riding Hood Have Been So Very Good and Still Keep the Wolf From the Door?" were outlawed. Radio output became very mellow, almost bland. The national networks could not afford to offend any of their family audience.

* An obscure village in Dorset, England.

"She's A New Kind Of Old-Fashioned Girl"(1929) assures parents that the new liberated flapper is a God-fearing woman, just like her mother, underneath the paint. It's in the same vein as "Glad Rag Doll" but, unfortunately, never really sold. I've heard a marvellous recording by "Whispering" Jack Smith in which, with a pacifying doctor's bedside manner, he speaks a little poem to the melody:

> Nothing is wrong with the girl of today,
> Why get away from the truth?
> Mothers who fret over daughters who pet
> Did the same thing in their youth.
> It isn't the lipstick, the cocktails, the jazz,
> If some girl should happen to fall —
> It's the mother who says, "If you're not home at ten
> You don't have to come home at all."
> There's many a girl on the wrong road tonight
> Who would have and could have been good,
> And each one is a living mistake of parents who misunderstood.
> So make a pal of your daughter — tell her what's what
> And don't hide that book on the shelf,
> Because the girl of today is wise to the ways of the world
> And can always take care of herself.

Finally, "I Love my Baby," a song that has lasted because, like most standards, it isn't dated by its lyrics. Just a merry melody with a rave about a cute number. Harry Warren, who realized his potential writing for Hollywood musicals, contributed the lively tune with its surprise harmony in the opening bars of the chorus. Bud Green wrote the words of "I Love My Baby", and he told me the story behind the song one lunchtime at Jack Dempsey's Bar on Broadway, where grand old Alleymen are to be found sipping a spot of bouillon. It seems Bud and Harry and Al Dubin were all under contract to Shapiro Bernstein's, and Al had put some words to a tune of Harry's — "Ain't I Got Rosie, Ain't Rosie Got Me". A cute idea but the publisher didn't care for the line which went, "I drive a truck — but who wouldn't for her?" Bud Green clocked out and caught the train home to Jersey. The tune kept buzzing round his head and suddenly a new title came to him — "I Love My Baby". Obviously that had to be followed by "My Baby loves me" and everything was smooth sailing after that. The boys at work loved the number. "A perfect marriage of words and music," they opined. Next day Cliff *Ukulele Ike) Edwards dropped in to seek out material for his Ziegfeld Follies show, heard "Baby" and included it in his act. Socko — he recorded the song and it did well. Fred Waring's Pennsylvanians featured it too, and got good response. And then everyone sang it. "The rest is history," said Bud, and got back to his bouillon.

AIN'T WE GOT FUN

Words by
GUS KAHN and
RAYMOND B. EGAN
English Version by RALPH STANLEY

Music by
RICHARD A. WHITING

Ain't we got fun

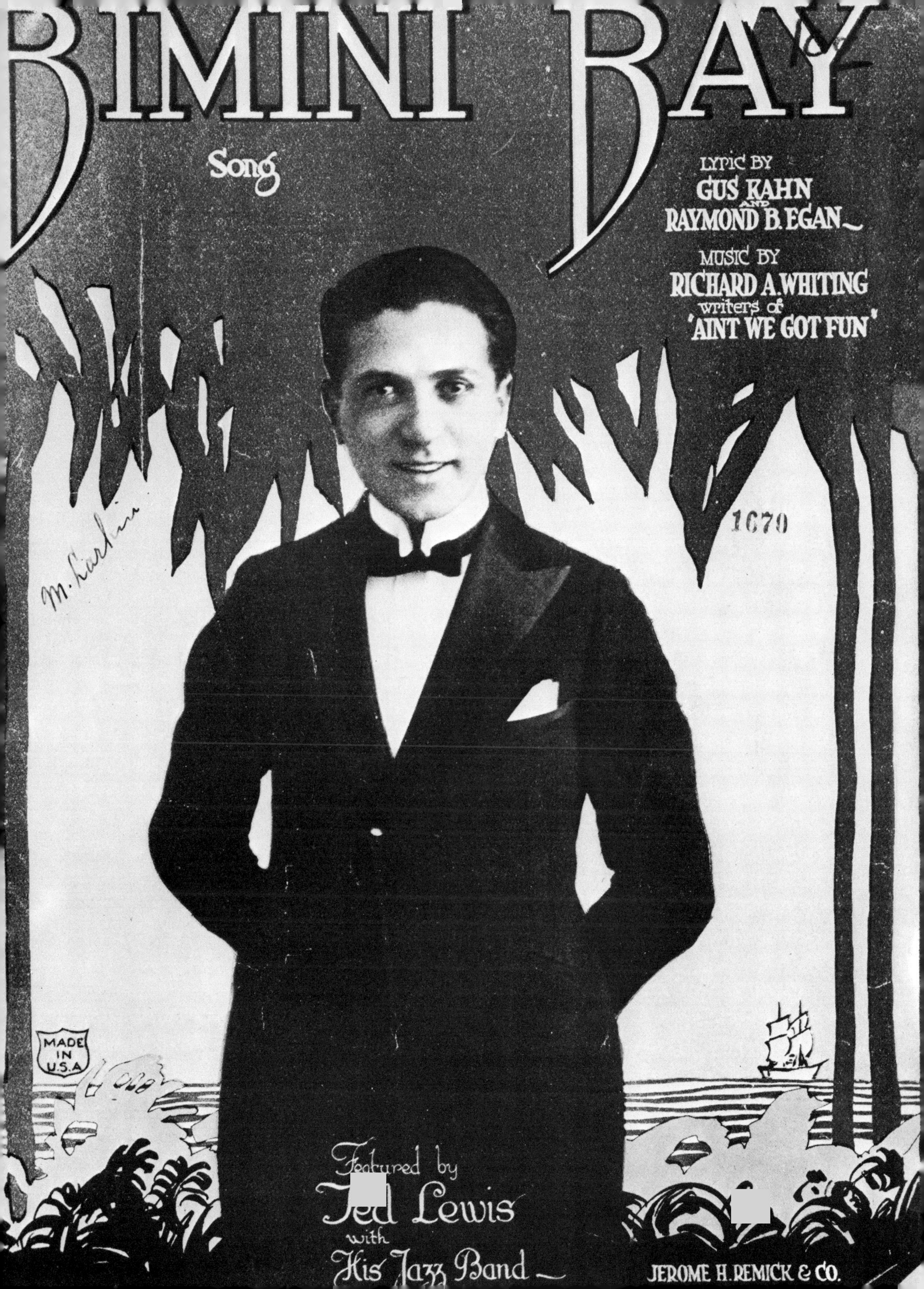
BIMINI BAY
Song
LYRIC BY
GUS KAHN
AND
RAYMOND B. EGAN
MUSIC BY
RICHARD A. WHITING
writers of
'AINT WE GOT FUN'
1670
MADE IN U.S.A
Featured by
Ted Lewis
with
His Jazz Band
JEROME H. REMICK & CO.

BIMINI BAY
SONG

Lyric by
GUS KAHN and
RAYMOND B. EGAN

Music by
RICHARD A. WHITING

Gad-a-bouts of now-a-days All spend their winter
There is mag-ic in the moon That makes De-cem-ber

hol - i - days___ Way down old Bim-in-i way___
seem like June___ Way down old Bim-in-i way___

3

4

CHORUS

Come and spoon with me   'Neath the jul-ep tree   Down old Bimini   way
There's a   rick-ey-tree   By the Hen-ne-sea   Down old Bimini   way

Hear the cock-tails a - call - ing   Come to Bim-in-i   Bay
All   the folks are good mix - ers   Down on Bim-in-i   Bay

Sweet or - ange   blos-soms a - wait you down yon - - der
You'll love that   top - i - cal trop - i - cal   Is - - land

Where they say   Ab-sinthe will make ev-'ry   lov - ing   heart grow fond - er
The moon shines bright ev-'ry night on that   love - ly   Rock and Rye - land

STUMBLING

A FOX TROT ODDITY

Words and Music by
"Zez" Confrey

POPULAR   EDITION
LEO. FEIST INC. NEW YORK
CANADA, LEO. FEIST, LIMITED, 193 YONGE ST. TORONTO.
FRANCIS, DAY & HUNTER, 138-140 CHARING CROSS ROAD, LONDON, ENG.

STUMBLING

A Unique Fox Trot Song
With an Original Rhythm

Words and Music by
ZEZ CONFREY

'Ten - tion folks,__ speak of jokes,__ This is one on me,__
Young and small__ short and tall,__ Folks most ev -'ry-where,__

Took my gal__ to a dance__ At the Ar-mo-ry,__
Take a chance__ do this dance,__ They think it's a bear,__

Mus - ic played,__ danc - ers swayed,__ Then we joined the crowd;__
Peo - ple rave__ and they crave__ Just to do this step,__

CHORUS

5021-3

5021-3

Written by
LEW BROWN.

Composed by
ALBERT VON TILZER.

1. Dap-per Dan was a Pull-man por-ter man On a
2. Dap-per Dan was a ve-ry hand-y man On a

train that ran thro' Dix-ie.   Ev-'ry one knew Dap-per Dan,   Knew him for a
train that ran thro' Dix-ie.   Made the beds and ev-'ry-thing,   All you had to

la-dies man.   Nev-er car'd   to set-tle down, Had a gal in ev-'ry
do was ring.   If the train stopp'd an-y-where There'd be some gal wait-ing

town.   On the train the whole day   long   You'll   hear him sing this   song_____
there.   He'd say "This is one of   mine,   And there's oth-ers down the   line._____

wait - in'   Down in sun - ny Car - o - line _____ Now I ain't hand - some,
wait - in'   Down in sun - ny New - Or - leans _____ I won't let no gal

I ain't sweet, But I've got a brand of lov - in' that can't be beat, I'm the la - dies' man from
run my life _ 'Cause if I lose them all I've still got my wife, I'm the la - dies' man from

1.
dear old Dix - ie - land." _____ "If I land."
dear old Dix - ie - land." _____ "If I land."

2.

D.C.

(ENGLISH VERSION)
By GEORGE ARTHURS

1

Dapper Dan was a gay commercial man,
And he travelled round the country.
Ev'ryone knew Dapper Dan,
Knew him for a ladies' man.
Never cared to settle down,
Had a girl in ev'ry town.
On the train the whole day long
You'd hear him sing this song.

CHORUS.
"If I lose my girl in Shrewsbury
   That won't worry me,
'Cause I've got another honey lamb
Waiting for me down in Birmingham.
And if I lose my girl in Birmingham
   I won't feel blue,
Cause I've got one in Blackpool
   That I can march right to.
If I lose my girl in Blackpool
   Bet that I won't pine,
'Cause I've got another girlie waiting
   In Newcastle on the Tyne.
Now, I'm not handsome, I'm not sweet,
But I've got a brand of loving that can't be beat.
I'm the ladies' man from dear old ✝London Town!"

2

Dapper Dan was a very clever man,
And he travelled round the country,
With his samples in his case,
Round for orders he would chase.
If the train stopped anywhere
There'd be some girl waiting there.
He'd say "This is one of mine,
And I've others down the line.

CHORUS.
"If I lose my girl in Aberdeen
   I won't make a scene,
'Cause I've got another as a rule
Waiting for me down in Liverpool,
And if I lose my girl in Liverpool
   I'll never fret.
'Cause I've got one in Dover
   That I can go and get.
If I lose my girl in Dover
   You bet I won't frown,
There's another loving girlie waiting
   Down in sunny Brighton Town.
I won't let women run my life,
'Cause if I lose them all I've still got my wife,
I'm the ladies' man from dear old ✝London Town!"

✝ *The Singer may substitute the name of any other place for local effect.*

F & D 15858

HENDERSON & SPALDING Lᵀᴰ Printers
Sylvan Grove London S.E.15

No. 1833.

Francis, Day & Hunter.
Regd No 257, 748.
Sixpence Nett.

7/2

CAROLINA IN THE MORNING.

SONG FOX-TROT

WRITTEN BY
GUS KAHN.
COMPOSED BY
WALTER DONALDSON.

Photo by Dobsons Studios.

SUNG BY

DOROTHY WARD.

6d NET.

FRANCIS, DAY & HUNTER,
138-140, CHARING CROSS ROAD, LONDON, W.C.2.

Copyright 1922, by Jerome H. Remick & Co., New York & Detroit.

PRINTED IN ENGLAND.

Carolina In The Morning

Written by GUS KAHN

CHORUS

Moderato

Tune Ukulele

4 3 2 1

G C E A

See back page for Introduction and Verse

Composed by WALTER DONALDSON

3

INTRODUCTION and VERSE

Moderato

1 Wish - ing is good time wast - ed, Still it's a hab - it, they say.
2 Dream - ing was meant for night - time; I live in dreams all the day.

Wish - ing for sweets I've tast - ed That's all I do__ all day
I know it's not the right time, But still I dream a - way.

May - be there's noth - ing in wish - ing, But speak - ing of wish - ing, I'll say
What could be sweet - er than dream - ing, Just dream - ing and drift - ing a - way?

Back to Chorus

ANY PLACE WHERE I MAKE MONEY
(IS HOME SWEET HOME TO ME)

WORDS BY
Wm. TRACEY
MUSIC BY
DAN DOUGHERTY

PUBLISHED BY
GOODMAN & ROSE INC.
222 WEST 46TH STREET, NEW YORK

ANY PLACE WHERE I MAKE MONEY
(IS HOME SWEET HOME TO ME)

Words by
Wᵐ TRACEY

Music by
DAN DOUGHERTY

I've al-ways been a ro - ver; I ne-ver set-tled down.
I've ne-ver felt real lone-some; I'm ne-ver wear-ing a frown.

I could ne-ver hon-est-ly say I had the blues for my home town.
I can al-ways man-age to make a lot of friends in ev'-ry town.

When a-ny place don't suit me, I ne-ver wor-ry or sigh; I
There is-n't a-ny one place That I could say I liked best; If

pack my grip and pay my bill and bid that place good-bye._____
things go right I'm hap-py in the North, South, East or West._____

CHORUS

I'm as much at home in Cal-i-for-nia as I am in Ten-ne-see.

_____ If there's a wel-come writ-ten on the mat _____ That's the

place I hang my coat and hat._____ I've lived in towns where the

lights are bright, And they ne-ver think it's late, _____ And in burgs where they pull in the

Any Place Where, etc 4

4

side - walks Ev'-ry night at half past eight.___ Oh, I

wish I had some-bo-dy wait - ing but I'm just a roll-ing stone

___ And Home Sweet Home is just a mel-o - dy.

Now
The

There are ma - ny things that you can o - ver look   As long as you can fat - ten up your
town may be a small one and the folks a scream, But I'd rath-er be a big fish in a
Love means more than mon - ey some poor nuts in-sist, But you can't pay an -y land-lords with a

To Patter *Fine*

pocket book
lit-tle streamSo an-y place where I make money is Home Sweet Home to me.   me.
hug and kiss

PATTER *4 times*

I'm con-ten-ted a - ny place I chance to be   As long as I get plen-ty of the
There's a les-son ev'-ry-bod-y ought to learn To keep a dol-lar out of ev'-ry
When you're wealthy ev-ry-bod-y wants to know What you do and how you came to
When you get a bank roll piled up on the shelf   Step right out and start in to en-

do ray me.   Mo-ney is the root of ev-il,   so they say;   I
two you earn.   Save a lit-tle for a rai-ny   day some-how; It's
make your dough.   Peo-ple start to pan you ev'-ry   place you walk But
joy your-self.   'Cause if you keep work-ing 'till your race you've run   You

1.2.3.   *4*

wish I had a-bout a mill-ion roots to-day.
get-ting kind of cloud-y and I'm start-ing now.   *D.S. al Fine*
if you've got it, you should wor-ry,   let 'em talk.
die and then your rel-a-tives have   all the fun. Oh I

Any Place Where, etc 4

SHE'S A NEW KIND OF OLD-FASHIONED GIRL

Words By
BILLY ROSE

Music By
VINCENT ROSE

PUBLISHED IN GREAT BRITAIN
BY
FRANCIS, DAY & HUNTER LTD.,
138, 140, CHARING CROSS ROAD,
LONDON, W.C.2.

Published By
IRVING BERLIN, Inc.

1607 Broadway   New York

MADE IN U. S. A.

SHE'S A NEW KIND OF OLD-FASHIONED GIRL

Words By
BILLY ROSE

Music By
VINCENT ROSE

crit - i - cize____ her mas - ca - ra'd eyes____ are too
paint - ed rose____ In her heart she knows____ lots of

hard on the girl of to - day____
things that you can't learn in books:____

Chorus

She's a new kind of old fash - ioned girl____

____ likes to play a - round____ cab - a - ret a-

- 3 -

fling_____ does-n't mean a thing_____

_____ Just as wise as her broth-er and as good as her

moth-er she's a new kind of old fash-ioned

girl_____ She's a girl_____

I Love My Baby
(My Baby Loves Me)

Uke in B♭
With Piano Tune thus

F B♭ D G

Words by
BUD GREEN

Music by
HARRY WARREN

Allegro moderato

Talk a - bout your fam - ous love af - fairs_____ Rom-e - o and
Tho' we've known each oth - er just a year_____ I'm not gon-na

Ju - li - et had theirs_____ I just found some one and
lose her, nev-er fear_____ Pa says I'm fool - ish and

some-one found me   We're not ver-y   fam-ous, but who   cares?_____ _____

Ma says so, too   'Cause each ev-'ning   this is what they   hear:_____

CHORUS

I love my ba - by   My ba-by loves me,

Don't know no - bod - y   As hap - py as   we   She's on - ly

We're hot - sy tot - sy   Why shouldn't we   be?   She gives me

twen-ty And I'm twen-ty - one ___   We ain't got mon-ey   But

kiss-es Each one is a smack_   But you should hear 'em   When

ain't us got fun ___ Some-times we quar — rel
I give 'em back ___ She bought a cook-book

And may-be we fight But,then we make up The fol-low-ing
She's learn-ing to bake I likeher cof — fee It keeps us a-

night When we're to - geth-er we're great com-pan-y ___
wake We wash the dish-es from sev - en to three ___ I love my

ba — by My ba-by loves me. ___

Alleymen
and theater writers

After Bud Green had told me about "I Love My Baby" we all stood up in Jack Dempsey's Bar. Edgar Leslie, the current dean of Alley writers, was slowly processing toward our table and as he recognized me a glitter came into his old eyes. A glitter not for my song scholarship but for the fact that I was a potential singer of Leslie material. Almost ninety but still the business juices flowed! "Let me tell you about this number," he growled, as he waved for his tea. "It was a big one for your own Jack Hylton — "Me And Jane In A Plane" — but, by Christ, this'll be a hit all over again in my astronaut version. See, I changed the lyrics." Then he sang it to me as he fiddled with his bread, but I was keen to discover how he came to write "When Ragtime Rosie Ragged The Rosary". "Get yourself a group called The Space Lads and record it, because it's only twelve bars long." "But I haven't got a group." "Just whistle down in Harlem." "But do tell me about Ragtime Rosie. Don't you like it?" "Sure I like it but it's too long and it's comedy and that won't sell today."

Edgar wrote words. One of his early hits was with Irving Berlin: "Sadie Salome Go Home". He went on to write "He'd Have To Get Under Get Out And Get Under", "For Me And My Gal", "Among My Souvenirs", "Pasadena" and dozens more. His favorite song is "The Lost Chord", and as for Shakespeare — "He doesn't bother me". I saw Bud and Edgar out of the bar and into the Broadway rain, dodging another old-timer I'd spied steaming towards me with manuscript gripped tightly, and thought how glad I was that in their twilight years these men who've given us so much pleasure in dance-hall, drawing-room and elevator can enjoy their fruits in a relaxed atmosphere. For these were men who sweated in visors in tiny cubicles for grasping publishers. Some songwriters had to pawn their own underwear. Henry Osgood, a visiting writer in the 1920's, described a pop publishing house as similar to an "extra noisy hour at the psychopathic ward in Bellevue Hospital". Kindly publishers provided fountains whose tinkles, gurgles and splashes made for an atmosphere conducive to poetic but commercial thoughts. These days a similar effect is obtained through well-placed tanks of tropical fish. In Nashville, one of the most successful publishing houses believes in abstract metal sculptures in a windowless building.

Wherever Alleymen gather the name of Walter Donaldson invariably comes up. A married man, he liked to travel with a shapely nurse. A man rich through song royalties, he never seemed to have a penny on him. "Lock away the suitcases — Uncle Walt's coming to stay," ordered the wife of one lyricist, for she knew that Donaldson liked to purloin these. Like many

Edgar Leslie, a charter member of ASCAP, started writing words to hits back in the ragtime era. His collaborators include Irving Berlin, Jimmy Monaco, Walter Donaldson, Harry Warren. His hits include "He'd Have To Get Under", "America, I Love You", "For Me and My Gal", "Home In Pasadena", "Dirty Hands, Dirty Face", "Among My Souvenirs", "Masculine Women And Feminine Men". His favorite song: "The Lost Chord". *Edgar Leslie*

Pioneers of Crooning: Whispering Jack Smith, Gene Austin, Rudy Vallee, Ruth Etting. *E.M.I. Publishing, Wildcroft Pix*

a songwriter he loved to gamble. Horses, cards, the weather. But every day at crack of dawn he sat down and wrote a song.* Yet "My Blue Heaven" (written in 1924, but not a hit till 1927) was composed in Donaldson's head while waiting for a free pool-table after lunch one day at The Friar's Club, New York. Vaudevillian George Whiting penned some words hymning domestic bliss and introduced the number in his stage act. Nothing doing. Timing is so important in pop, but who knows the right time? It wasn't until Gene Austin made a suave recording of it in 1927 that the song caught fire and "My Blue Heaven" became the first million-selling vocal disc. Like many of Donaldson's luller songs, "Heaven" plays much on the sixth note of the scale. That's a winner note in pop music.

In 1927 Donaldson, now chief of his own company, wrote the score for *Whoopee*, a Broadway musical starring Eddie Cantor. Just before opening night they needed a vehicle for

---

*He was as generous with songs as with golf balls: his daily average was twenty-four balls in the pond; he gave as many publishers percentages of each song.

98

Ruth Etting, and Donaldson knocked off what he considered a rotten egg because of some sort of tiff he was having with the management. The song was "Love Me or Leave Me" — and I don't believe a word of that story. It's a magnificent tune of octave leaps and chromatic crawls, with a crafty harmony that tilts with unobtrusive suddenness into another key, from minor to major. Jazz players love it.

Gus Kahn's words to "Love Me or Leave Me" are in the "torch" tradition. A lovelorn girl carrying in her heart an ever-burning flame for a lost love — that was the torch idea, and it began in America with an imported song called "Mon Homme", just after the war. The French are adept at this breast—heaving but Ruth Etting, with her spaniel eyes and genuine experience of suffering at the hands of brutes, soon mastered the art of the clutched handkerchief: battered babies!

The Boss: Bing Crosby, known as "Der Bingle" in Germany. Disc buffs claim Crosby tones found ideal sympathy in bassy-sweet pre-hi-fi loudspeakers. *Wildcroft Pix*

The new liberated girls of the twenties had many a battered baby in their ranks. The man/woman battle was on! Countless Hollywood movies of the period show striding strapperettes competing with us, but *we* are stronger in body! Joan Crawford leading carloads of gay partygoers, first to plunge off the yacht at her undies party. Clara Bow, the It Girl, thwacking Gilbert Roland with her riding crop. Sirens tempting Al Jolson on to the purple path away from his mother. Then James Cagney giving Mae Clarke what-for with a grapefruit squelched full in her face. In "Love Me or Leave Me" the girl is happy to be unhappy as she mopes alone in her apartment reminiscing and regretting. Glorious self-pity — an emotion you'll rarely find in the black blues but a gorgeous emotion for all that.

On the couch with a suitor a girl listens to the love words and tries to make sure he really means he loves her before she takes the plunge: "Be sure it's true when you say 'I love you' — it's a sin to tell a lie". Billy Mayhew's "It's a Sin to Tell a Lie" (1936) was his only hit and an old-fashioned one musically. Full of barber-shop chords. The teenage Vera Lynn made a very sincere recording of it in Britain and the plea is pushed home all the more firmly by her forthright English accent. At the time most British singers were striving hard to sound American. I suppose they still are, except in comedy songs. Edgar Leslie was asked to tidy up the lyrics originally. "What the hell," he replied. "There's nothing I can do. The number stinks and it's a hit!"

In an age that was supposed to have been all-roaring with Charlestons and drunken orgies it's surprising how many of the hits were doleful. "Me and My Shadow" (1927), still a pub favorite, tells of a lonely bachelor plodding the streets on his way home to his gas-ring and empty bed. "Jim and Jack and John put their slippers on. They're all set but we're still on the go, so lonely." Why was it that the noble status of bachelor fell from favor? Billy Rose, the song's writer, wasn't writing from experience: he was ever under the bright lights of Broadway and playing the ladies. Note that Al Jolson gets a writer credit, which simply means he got a cut of the royalties for steadfastly plugging the song. This was an established payola practice of the day.

"Dream Train" (1928) didn't mean much saleswise. There's an excellent piano roll, though. I like the picture evoked of an ink-stained clerk returning nightly on the commuter train to his suburban home, supping off canned goods, suffering his wife's slings and arrows, and finally escaping in sleep down the night railway to a boyhood land where all is apple pie O.K.

In contrast to the ill-fated "Dream Train" is "I'll Get By" (1928), a true standard. Bing Crosby sang a rousing chorus on a contemporary recording with the Ipana Troubadours, and Connie Francis gave her hang-dog treatment on her late fifties hit record. The tune is sturdy and fresh: after hovering low on the opening lines of the chorus it suddenly soars off on " . . . as long as I", hits that melancholy augmented chord on "have" and the ever popular sixth chord on "you". Composer Fred Ahlert advised songwriters never to go higher than the E above middle C and though he sounds as if he's broken his rule here, his top note is that very E. At the time of "I'll Get By" he was a full-time arranger with Irving Aaronson's Commanders. Originally he turned in a song of the normal thirty-two bar length. Pop songs had settled down to this shape, probably because it suited dance bands and record companies and businessmen publishers. And thirty-two bar songs are very comfortable somehow. But Ahlert decided to be perverse and sliced down his tune to twenty-eight bars, much to the shock of the publishers. They pleaded, they begged, but Ahlert would not give in. His stocky, odd little tune appealed to the mysterious public and everyone heaved a sigh of relief. "I'll Get By" is a street phrase. *Slang.* "Dream Train" is a brain phrase. *Fantasy.* Many, many hits consist of street slang put to music: "Jeepers Creepers," "Anything Goes", "A-Tisket A-Tasket", "Yakety Yak", "Woolly Bully", and so on. In the forties the publishers decided to alter the words "Poverty may come to me, it's true" to "though

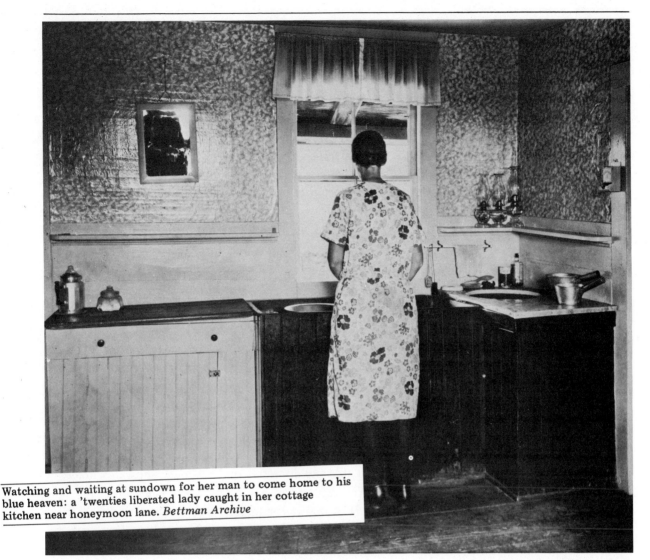

Watching and waiting at sundown for her man to come home to his blue heaven: a 'twenties liberated lady caught in her cottage kitchen near honeymoon lane. *Bettman Archive*

I may be far away," as a war concession. I prefer "poverty" because it's an unusual word in pop music.

"Chloe" (1927) is an odd girl. I have asked the composer's son and the lyricist's son about why this strange subject of swamp love was chosen but neither of them know. They assure me though, that "Chloe" was a galloping smash. I've put two and two together and maybe made three, but here's what I'd guess. The song melodrama is probably inspired by the Jerome Kern/ Oscar Hammerstein success *Showboat* (1927), a tale of the Old South. Perhaps two Alley laborers hoped they might catch some ripples? Also, Neil Moret's publishing house was in San Francisco and reasonably close to Hollywood. Was this an embryonic theme song for a swamp movie? At any rate, with its thunder, howls, moaning wind and slow drag rhythm it's an oddity. Completely theatrical — and I love the number. Paul Whiteman's band made a symphonic arrangement, and much later Spike Jones and his City Slickers parodied poor Chloe and she has never been the same. The present copyright owners tell me that since the Spike Jones record royalties have drastically dropped.

Just as comedians long to play Hamlet so Alleymen longed to elevate themselves into theater music. To leave the sweat-life of having to whip out instant single-song hits and bask in the leisure and dignity of musical comedy, a breath away from opera. Irving Berlin, one-time singing waiter and Alley worker, made the grade. So, most notably, did George

Gershwin, whose initial pop excitement was caused by Jerome Kern's "They Didn't Believe Me". Serving an apprenticeship in the Alley he and his collaborator Irving Caesar were asked to write a one-step in the style of "Hindustan", a raging success at the time (1919). They Americanized the eastern novelty by setting their song in Stephen Foster-land. "Swanee" (1919) was written in fifteen minutes at Gershwin's New York apartment. There was an evening poker game in progress at the time so George and Irving curtained off an area and set to work. When it was finished the poker players were asked to form an impromptu orchestra in order to perform the new work. Gershwin's father played an obbligato part on comb and lavatory paper to George's deft piano.

"Swanee" was used, initially, as a production number in a revue at the vast Capitol Theater. A flock of leggy beauties tapped away to it, but though the applause was deafening there were no sales. Harms, the publishers, stopped their plugging. But three months later the indefatigable George was, as usual, monopolizing the piano at a party, and Al Jolson heard "Swanee" only a few times before he surrendered and stuck it in his new Winter Garden revue. Sales soared. Much later George and Irving took a first trip to the South and had a hasty glimpse at the muddy stream which had formed the title of their big hit. "I was shocked," Irving Caesar told me once. "But I'm a craftsman like, say, a carpenter who puts in a good job whether it be carving a door for a palace or a whorehouse."

The tune fairly strides along, elbowing almost. "You gotta hear what I gotta say." A bit Russian at times, and certainly not Southern, and yet how very American that three Jews (two of Russian extraction) should have been responsible for such a slice of Americana!

Gershwin went on to write highly acclaimed musical comedies and even an opera, *Porgy and Bess*. But "Swanee", that quarter-hour trifle, remains his best seller. Richard Rodgers and Lorenz Hart started out as uppity Ivy League students, contemptuous of our Alleymen. Speaking of those days (in 1918) when they first collaborated on university shows, Rodgers pointed out that "before Hart, only P.G. Wodehouse had made any real assault on the intelligence of the song-listening public . . . Hart knew, for instance, that love was not especially devised for boy and girl idiots of fourteen and he expressed himself to that extent."

Their early efforts were full of tricksy rhymes set to simple, almost lackadaisical music. Too clever-clever perhaps. But a perfect little jewel of a song, "Manhattan," in an intimate revue called *The Garrick Gaieties*(1925), burst out to become their first hit. The two writers were astounded that the public should take to such sophistication. After all, this mass had been basking vicariously in "Swanee" and "Hindustan", or in Kentucky, Araby, Athlone, Carolina or Hawaii, so what could be romantic about New York, outside of Broadway? Hart pokes gentle fun at the Alley's faraway places songs and at New York: the balmy breezes of the charming subway, the adventure of trying to cross Fifth Avenue, the sight of bearded artists in Greenwich Village "where modern men itch to be free." It's not "ho-ho" humor but it's smart and cunning.

Rodgers's tune is pretty without being cloying and just different enough from the average pop song to stick out. The first two bars are standard stuff, but just as you're expecting the normal pop form Rodgers gives you three G's on "island too." Pleasant presents. The minor seventh, that ambivalent chord, crops up a lot here — a presage of things to come in theater music. Theater composers became fond of the minor seventh's insouciance. The opposite effect of Jolson's heart-on-sleeve songs.

Eventually, however, success met success as it will in the tiny world of show business. In 1930 Rodgers and Hart were lured to Hollywood, where they did most of their work for the next seven years. Jolson himself starred in an experimental picture, *Hallelujah,*

I'm A Bum, for which they wrote the music. Even the dialogue was sung. The overall artiness turned off moviegoers. Then the songwriters had trouble with a Jean Harlow picture-song known variously as "Oh, Lord, Why Won't You Make Me A Star?" and "The Bad in Every Man". The song kept getting bumped off the picture. So they retitled it "Blue Moon" and released it as a plain ordinary pop song. There, in the bustling pop market, it shot up to the top and has stayed. Beloved of rock 'n rollers, "Blue Moon" has been a hit for the Marcels and has even been recorded by Bob Dylan. The chord sequence was adopted by many rhythm and blues writers for their love ballads, and can also be found supporting such teen hits as "Who Put The Bomp?", "Diana", "Rubber Ball", "Little Darlin'", 'Speedy Gonzales", and many more.

Since the end of the Great War Britain had become the dumping ground for American films, shows and pop songs and pop styles. Music hall was fighting a rearguard action, but songs about fish and pies and Leicester Square couldn't compete with the slick, well-packaged American all-purpose song. And, of course, jazz appealed instantly to those who wished to be modern or to escape the dreariness of European life. Clearly, Europe was no longer the center of the world.

Britain had no musical equivalent to jazz. Folk music had withered with industrialism and no amount of massaging by earnest Hampstead herbalist revivalists could bring it back. Only in musical comedy had we made our mark, almost established a style: in Gilbert and Sullivan, in the gay soufflés of Paul Rubens, Leslie Stuart and Lionel Monckton — shows that almost invariably had "girl" or "maid" in the title. These entertainments, admired and imitated by Broadway, were the invention of impresario George Edwardes: "A happy compromise between the continental operettas of Lecocq and Offenbach, the early burlesques of the old Gaiety theater and the healthy, clean-limbed but melodious high jinks of Gilbert and Sullivan."

Noel Coward wrote that. He kept the tradition afloat through the jazz age and swing age, writing both romantic operetta-like songs ("I'll See you Again", "Lover Of My Dreams") and jazzy songs ("Twentieth Century Blues", "Dance Little Lady"), taking his light music seriously yet always able, like Cole Porter and Lorenz Hart, to stand just outside the show-biz flurry and comment or criticize gently. This is a characteristic not found much in the world of Tin Pan Alley; the hustlers haven't the time or vantage point to observe their absurdity, or the world's absurdity. Perhaps the homosexuality of Coward, Hart and Porter, marking them as social outlaws (however concealed), helped to give them the view through the window into the party.

"Parisian Pierrot" (1923) is early Coward and simple in outlook: the gay gamin butterfly whose fluttery days are numbered — a favorite situation for Alley writers ("Poor Butterfly", "Glad Rag Doll"). Set in his key of E flat (he was an ear composer and had each note taken down by his music secretary), the tune is rich but not too fat to move, so is quite danceable. The shape of the chorus must have influenced Isham Jones in "It Had To Be You". Coward's ballads lent themselves to enshrinement as standards, while his comedy songs (like "Mad Dogs") seem to sag when performed by anyone else but the Master.

All in all, though I admire and respect the song jewelers of theaterland, they had a much softer time than our Alleymen, who were like surfers catching the new waves of pop. Rodgers and Hart, Cole Porter and Noel Coward weren't in love with jazz and the big beat. They disliked danceband treatments of their songs. *Cavalcade* can be viewed as Noel Coward's warning of the chaos wrought by Afro-American music, harbinger of the break-up of the Old World and its values.

My Blue Heaven

A FASCINATING FOX TROT BALLAD
With Ukulele Accompaniment

by
WALTER DONALDSON
Writer of "AT SUNDOWN"

LYRIC by
GEORGE WHITING

Featured by
GUS ARNHEIM
and his
Orchestra

"You can't go wrong
with any FEIST" song

POPULAR — EDITION
LEO. FEIST INC. NEW YORK
CANADA, LEO. FEIST, LIMITED, 193 YONGE ST., TORONTO

MY BLUE HEAVEN

Written by
GEORGE WHITING

Tune
Ukulele

Composed by
WALTER DONALDSON

Bb Eb G C

Moderato

1. Day is end — ing, Birds are wend — ing Back to the shel — ter
2. Moon - beams creep — ing, Flow'rs are sleep — ing Un — der a star - lit

of Each lit-tle nest they love. Night - shades fall — ing,
way, Wait-ing an - oth - er day. Time for rest — ing,

F. & D. Ltd. 18079

FRANCIS, DAY & HUNTER, Ltd. 138-140, Charing Cross Rd. London.W.C.2.

3

Love - birds call - ing, What makes the world go round? Noth-ing but love! _____
Birds are nest - ing, Rest-ing their wea - ry wings, Tired from play. _____

CHORUS

When Whip-poor-wills call _____ and ev'ning is nigh _____ I hur-ry to

my blue heav - en. A turn to the right, _____

_ a lit-tle white light _____ Will lead you to my blue

4

heaven. You'll see a smil-ing face, a fire-place, a co-sy room,

A lit-tle nest that's nes-tled where the ros-es bloom. Just Mol-lie and

me _____ And Ba-by makes three, _____ We're hap-py in my

blue ___ heav-en. When Whip-poor-wills blue heav-en.

D.S.

Printed in England by WEST CENTRAL PRINTING CO. LTD. London.

F. & D. Ltd. 18079

Love Me Or Leave Me

★ Piano Accordion

Lyric by
GUS KAHN

Music by
WALTER DONALDSON

Chorus-Slowly *(with feeling)*

LOVE ME OR LEAVE ME, and let me be lone - ly;

You won't be-lieve me, and I love you on - ly; I'd rath - er be lone - ly, than

hap-py with some-bod-y else. ___ You might find the night-time, the

right time for kiss - ing; But night-time is my time for just rem - i - nis-cing, Re-

gret-ting, in-stead of for - get-ting with some-bod-y else. ___

INTRODUCTION and VERSE

Moderato

1. Shades of night are fall-ing and I'm lone - ly, _____
2. When the sun sets on the far ho - ri - zon _____

Stand-ing on the cor-ner feel-ing blue. _____   Sweet-hearts, out for fun,
And the par-lour lamps be-gin to glow, _____   Jim and Jack and John

Pass me one by one,   Guess I'll wind up like I al-ways do, with   on - ly
Put their slip-pers on,   They're all set, but we're still on the go, so   lone-ly,

Back to Chorus

F. & D. Ltd. 22088

Printed in England by WEST CENTRAL PRINTING CO. LTD. London.

I'LL GET BY

(AS LONG AS I HAVE YOU)

FEATURED IN

"A GUY NAMED JOE"

WITH

IRENE DUNNE and SPENCER TRACY

A
METRO-GOLDWYN-MAYER
PICTURE

Lyric by
OY TURK

Music by
ED AHLERT

I'LL GET BY
(As Long As I Have You)

Featured in "A GUY NAMED JOE"
A METRO GOLDWYN MAYER PICTURE - Starring
SPENCER TRACY - IRENE DUNNE

Lyric by
ROY TURK

Music by
FRED E. AHLERT

* Symbols for Guitar, Chords for Ukulele and Banjo

I'll Get By-2

It's A Sin To Tell A Lie.

Words and Music by
BILLY MAYHEW.
Additional Lyric by Charles Wilmott

Copyright 1936, by Donaldson, Douglas & Gumble, Inc.,1619, Broadway. N.Y.

F.& D.Ltd.20144

3

P. & D. Ltd. 20144.

A WORTH WEIL SONG

Dream Train

WORDS BY
CHARLES NEWMAN
MUSIC BY
BILLY BASKETTE

Ruth Cook Thori

My favorite song "Dream Train" Guy Lombardo

MILTON WEIL MUSIC CO INC
54 W. Randolph St CHICAGO.
MADE IN U.S.A.

Dream Train

Piano Tune Uke in D

A   D   F#   B

Words by
CHARLES NEWMAN

A Rube Bennett Arrangement

Music by
BILLY BASKETTE

go to Par - a - dise, _____
days that used to be, _____

Sand-man is the en - gi - neer when my train pulls a - way, ___ Ev'- ry
On my train of dreams I'll soon be on my mer - ry way, ___ To the

night he hears me say; _____
on - ly place for me; _____

Dream Train - 4

4

CHORUS

Tenderly

DREAM TRAIN please car-ry me back, ___

DREAM TRAIN stay on the right track, ___

Take me back where I be-long, ___ Sound your

whis-tle and gong, tell the gang it wont be long,

DREAM TRAIN please turn on your steam,— Morn-ing will soon end my dream,— Stop! when a sweet old la-dy hol-lers "Wel-come" My DREAM —— TRAIN. —— TRAIN.

RAYNER, DALHEIM & CO.
MUSIC PRINTERS
CHICAGO

"I GOT TO GO WHERE YOU ARE"

CHLO-E

(SONG OF THE SWAMP)

Lyric by
GUS KAHN

Music by
NEIL MORET

Villa Morét
Inc.
MUSIC PUBLISHERS
SAN FRANCISCO

BAUMER PIANO CO.
33 MAMARONECK AVENUE
WHITE PLAINS, NEW YORK

Sole Agents
EDWARD B. MARKS
MUSIC CORPORATION
R C A Bldg., Radio City, New York

CHLOE
(Song of the Swamp)

Written by
GUS KAHN

Composed by
NEIL MORÈT

Copyright 1927, by Villa Morèt, Inc., Pantages Building, San Francisco

F. & D. Ltd.

FRANCIS, DAY & HUNTER, Ltd. 138-140, Charing Cross Road, London. W. C. 2.

Empty spac-es meet his eyes, Emp-ty arms out stretched, "he's cry-in':-
Be no rest-in', got to go, Got to go and find my Chlo-e!"

mp

Am   Em   F   C   D9   D7   G7 dim G7 dim

rall.

REFRAIN

Slow Drag Rhythm

"Through the black of night, I got to go where you are;

mp–f

G7

If it's wrong or right, I got to go where you are ___ I'll

C7

C+

roam through the dis-tant swamp-land search-ing for you; 'Cause if

F   G7   C   Am   C+ C   D9

F. & D. Ltd.

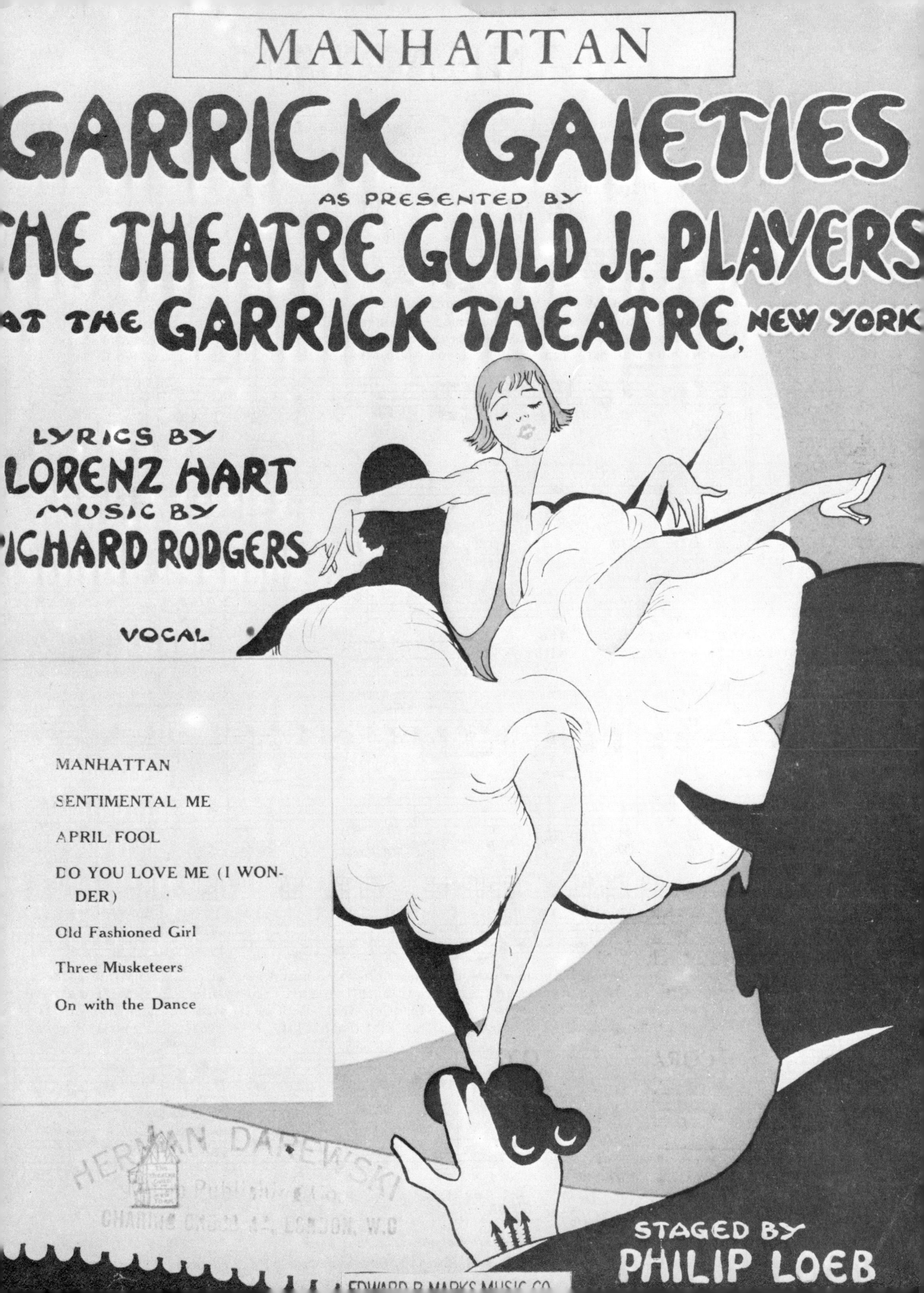

MANHATTAN

GARRICK GAIETIES

AS PRESENTED BY

THE THEATRE GUILD Jr. PLAYERS

at the **GARRICK THEATRE**, NEW YORK

LYRICS BY
LORENZ HART
MUSIC BY
RICHARD RODGERS

VOCAL

MANHATTAN

SENTIMENTAL ME

APRIL FOOL

DO YOU LOVE ME (I WON-
DER)

Old Fashioned Girl

Three Musketeers

On with the Dance

HERMAN DAREWSKI
CHARING CROSS RD, LONDON, W.C

EDWARD B. MARKS MUSIC CO.

STAGED BY
PHILIP LOEB

MANHATTAN

Words by LORENZ HART

Music by RICHARD RODGERS

Tune Ukulele — G C E A

See back page for Introduction and Verse

3

4

INTRODUCTION and VERSE

Moderato

Printed in England by WEST CENTRAL PRINTING CO. LTD. London.

F. & D. Ltd. 22455

2453

Blue Moon

Words by — Lorenz Hart.

Music by — Richard Rodgers.

LONDON: FRANCIS, DAY & HUNTER, Ltd.
138-140, CHARING CROSS ROAD, LONDON, W.C.2.

NEW YORK: METRO-GOLDWYN-MAYER, CORP.

Authorised for sale only in The British Empire
excepting Canada, Australia & New Zealand.

PRICE 6D NET

BLUE MOON.

Words by
LORENZ HART.

Music by
RICHARD RODGERS

PARISIAN PIERROT

NOEL COWARD.

AS SUNG IN
LONDON CALLING BY
GERTRUDE LAWRENCE

PARISIAN PIERROT.

NOEL COWARD.

K. P. & Cº 2704

Columbine and Pantaloon, A wistful Pierrot 'neath the moon, And Har-le-quin a rogue.
Pierrot in a tragic pose Will kiss a fa-ded sil-ver rose, With sadness in his heart.

Now-a-days Par-is-i-ans of leis-ure,
Some day soon he'll leave his tears be-hind him,

Wake the ec-ho of an old re-frain,
Com-e-dy comes laugh-ing down the street,

Each some ragged ef-fi-gy will
Col-um-bine will fly to him, ad-

treasure for his pleasure, Till the shad-ows of their sto-ry live a-gain. Par-is-i-an
-mir-ing and de-sir-ing, lay-ing love and ad-or-a-tion at his feet. Par-is-i-an

3

4

REFRAIN.

Pier - - rot____ So-ci - e-ty's he - - ro____ The Lord of a

day, The Rue de la Paix Is un-der your sway,____ The world may

L. H.

flat - - ter____ But what does that mat - - ter,____ They'll nev-er

shat - - ter____ your gloom pro - found,____ Par-is - i - an

5

From the Columbia Picture "THE JOLSON STORY"

SWANEE

Words by
I. CAESAR.

Tune Ukulele

Music by
GEORGE GERSHWIN

4

Printed in England by WEST CENTRAL PRINTING CO. LTD. London.

Movie melodies

The cinema is very dependent on popular music for mood evocation during the picture and in the light afterwards. What would *Casablanca* be without "As Time Goes By"? *The Third Man* without "The Harry Lime Theme"? *Butch Cassidy* without "Raindrops Keep Falling On My Head"? *The Sting* without Scott Joplin's rags? John Ford, in particular, was well aware of the power of old songs for instant period moods.

From the beginning the movie business was entangled with the pop business. Both were new rogue arts, outside the pale of respectable lines like banking and industry. Outcast Jewish immigrants flocked to the Alley and the flicker peep-show arcades. Movie moguls Jesse Lasky, Harry Cohn and Jack Warner all served in the Alley. Song pluggers were welcome at silent movie theaters where they led the audience in hearty choruses of their latest songs, accompanied by song slides on the screen, while the reels were changed or the fire doused. Later special cartoons were drawn to illustrate current hits with the screened lyrics dotted by a bouncing ball. There were tie-ups between song publishers and film companies, such as "Your Lips are No-Man's Land But Mine", which was sold wherever the film *Over The Top*, a Tommy's eye-witness account of the war, was shown. There were theme songs, the first being "Mickey" from *Mickey*, a Mabel Normand vehicle.

During the twenties cinemas became ornate Everyman's palaces, providing comfort and luxury for a few pence — and good music by fine orchestras. The Silent Cinema was never silent: features arrived with special scores for the resident orchestra, and if a theme song could be slotted in (marched for the martial sequences, slurped for the romance bits, and minor-keyed for the melodrama) so much the better. If the song was a hit, the film was a hit, if the film was a hit, the song was a hit — frequently.

In the mid-twenties Warner Brothers Pictures, a shoe-string company, started gambling with a process called Vitaphone, which was a rather primitive sound film, a projector being hooked up to a phonograph record (not a new invention at all: the system had been used back in the early 1900's). The Warners were desperate to try any novelty that might catch on and thus make them money, so that they could spend more time on the golf course, or playing cards, or horses. Films were potential celluloid money and only kooks studied films as art.

The Vitaphone shorts featured musical acts, some classical and some popular. Their Al Jolson short was a real moneyspinner. The Warners decided to pin their hopes on

popular music, so in 1927 they produced *The Jazz Singer*, a gooey cheesecake starring Al and silent except for some song sequences. In these Al encouraged the orchestra to "Get Hot!" and told the audience, "Wait a minute, wait a minute! You ain't heard nothing yet!" There was a long stretch of ad-libbing with his screen mother during "Blue Skies" and it was this that enthralled audiences. Silents were doomed. The All-Talking picture quickly arrived, closely followed by the All-Singing picture. Silent stars burst into song in mammoth Hollywood revues tacked together by the major studios. Much of the output was simply filmed theater but there were cinematic exceptions — for example, *Applause*, starring Helen Morgan, full of roaming cameras and careful cutting, directed by Rouben Mamoulian.

Hollywood needed cheap music and turned to Tin Pan Alley, now tottering under the impact of records and radio. Quickly the old companies were bought up by the movie-makers. By the end of the thirties the big Hollywood film companies owned most of the world's standard hit songs. Hollywood also lured the songwriters to take the train west and write songs for musicals, or even for any film. From 1929-31 no film was complete without a nightclub sequence in which a song was plugged. In 1932 a slump in film musicals occurred, but in 1933 Warner Brothers revived the form with *42nd Street*, an archetypal backstage story. From then on the film musical became a staple until the age of rock. At its best (say MGM's *Singin' In The Rain*) the Hollywood musical is the complete entertainment because it contains music, theater, painting, ballet and escape.

"At The Moving Picture Ball" (1920) is the Alley reflecting a current trend — it follows "Take Your Girlie To The Pictures If You Can't Make Love At Home". By 1920 the star system had already begun and fan magazines were flourishing. The tradition of setting songs at balls, and then describing the goings-on there, dates back in popular music history to the 1880's and such rowdy Irishy songs as "The Irish Jubilee". In the ragtime years, activities "At the Ragtime Ball", "At The Old Maid's Ball", "At The Devil's Ball", "At The Yiddishe Society Ball" were observed. We might note that "Moving Picture Ball" refers to not only film stars but back-room boys like producers Adolph Zukor and Jesse Lasky (founders of Paramount Pictures), William Fox (ill-starred founder of Fox Pictures) and pioneer director Thomas Ince, whose death in 1924 after a trip on the yacht of Press Baron William Randolph Hearst provided one of Hollywood's first unsolved mysteries. Wallace Reid, rugged screen hero mentioned in the song, came to a tragic end too: he overdosed on drugs, at a time when it was not the thing to do.

Theda Bara (real name Theodosia Goodman) was the first screen sex symbol. A vamp in the middle-eastern manner, she was very different from sweet "Charmaine" (1926), the French girl of the Great War who loved the doughboys. The song was the theme hit of the film *What Price Glory?* and played relentlessly through the story. The tune has a continental descent with an emphasis on that sad sweet-and-sour seventh note (the European equivalent to a blue note), so it's not surprising it was composed by Hungarian Erno Rapee (actually in 1913). He became the musical director at New York's sumptuous Radio City Music Hall, providing expensive scores for silent pictures.

Although *The Jazz Singer* was the film that turned people on to talkies, it wasn't a musical but a drama with occasional songs. The first screen musical was *Broadway Melody* (1929), made by MGM and starring Charles King, Bessie Love and Anita Page. Its story of unknowns making it big on Broadway was the model for subsequent backstage musicals.

The score was particularly rich in hits: "Broadway Melody", "The Wedding of the Painted Doll" (filmed in early color as a stage extravaganza on Ziegfeld lines) and "You Were

COMPLIMENTS OF

HOLLYWOOD BOULEVARD
ASSOCIATION
6605 Hollywood Blvd.
HOLLYWOOD CALIFORNIA

Picture Copyrighted 1928 Hollywood Boulevard Association

Wildcroft Pix

157

Meant For Me". "The Boy Friend", the other song, though peppy and jazzy and performed with coltish charm by Bessie and Anita, failed to hit.

"You Were Meant For Me" is introduced by Charles King (a highly animated Broadway vaude-thespian) in an apartment sequence where he is trying unsuccessfully to woo Anita Page. He's talking away and suddenly the orchestra chips in with an introduction so King bursts into song. In those days the orchestras were actually there on the set, just out of camera. Dubbing hadn't been perfected yet. The number obeys the rules laid down by its composer, the immaculate Nacio Herb Brown (incidentally, he was a Mexican and had started in real estate): ultra-simple repetitive melody, preferably all on the tonic and dominant chords (he sneaks in a few more here) spread out in wide interval leaps, with some "cry" lines like the chromatic descent on the words "Nature patterned you . . .". Arthur Freed's words are pretty functional, and altogether the song is a prime example of a slick Hollywood film song, just right for dance bands and crooners and street whistlers. Brown and Freed, the first songwriter kings of Hollywood, worked fast and easily, writing their scores rapid-fire a few weeks before shooting began on a picture that might have taken a year to set up. Wax-moustached Nacio Herb Brown was only too glad to finish his chores and get back to his main interests, which were collecting cars and girls and moving house. He was so busy decorating his houses that he only had time to stay married to Anita Page (also Mexican) for six months.

"Tip-toe Through The Tulips" (1929) is another early movie musical song. Nick Lucas, troubadour with a guitar, sang this in *The Gold Diggers Of Broadway*, a Vitaphone feature which also starred leggy Ann Pennington and dapper Conway Tearle. Dubin and Burke, two ex-Alleymen now operating on the West Coast, were adepts at pretty images in the rosy poetic manner, and in "Tip-toe" they came up with rather an English Edwardian musical comedy number. A jaunty tune with dainty touches and a lyric which seems almost prissy, with its apology for a sneaked kiss in the moonlit garden. Nick Lucas was far from being a wet crooner. He had, and still has, a virile stentorian voice capable of hitting the back seats of any theater. I recently provided the ukulele accompaniment for him when he belted the song out at a Santa Monica Music Hall. "Remember the chords," he advised me, "because they're awful good ones." And they are! "Tip-toe" was recorded by numerous singers apart from Lucas: Johnny Marvin, Irving Kaufman and much later, in the sixties, Helen Shapiro — and of course Tiny Tim. It's odd that the film companies didn't release their musical film sound tracks until the forties. With the exception of Warner Brothers, who owned both a radio station and (for a short time) Brunswick Records, Hollywood had no stake in radio or records. Of course, during the early thirties the record industry was in a frightful state and sales didn't get back to normal till the end of the decade.

When Warner Brothers bought Remick Music they got Harry Warren as part of the deal. He hated Los Angeles at first. He missed the old camaraderie of Lindy's in New York, where the writers swapped lines over coffee and cakes. His daily drive to Wanrer's Burbank studios was like a Western epic, fraught with danger. Rocks tumbled into the road sometimes. And when he got there the view from his cubby-hole office window was pure desert. However, there was the solace of Al Dubin, with whom he was teamed at once to write the songs for *42nd Street*. Musicals were supposedly dead in that year of 1933. But Daryl Zanuck rang the bell with *42nd Street.* A new era of musicals opened. Dubin and Warren worked steadily with dance sequence director Busby Berkeley, king of the kaleidoscope image. At least, they provided the songs and took them to Berkeley, who so often was waiting on the sound stage, worriedly tapping his riding breeches with a crop because he had

Mary Doran, Anita Page and Bessie Love show what they're made of in *Broadway Melody* (M.G.M. 1929), first sound film to win an Oscar and first of a blood of back-stage musicals. All songs by Nacio Herb Brown and Arthur Freed. *Kobal Collection*

392-89

"Tip-toe Through The Tulips" routine from *Gold Diggers of Broadway* (Warner Bros Vitaphone, 1929). *Kobal Collection*

several dozen girlies, some fountains and maybe a few greyhounds and *no music*. Once he got the song he could set about visualizing Dubin's words. The songs were romantic, but Berkeley roved over the winsomely sexy statued girlies with a caressing camera. Harry Warren didn't hang around to socialize; he was off home early and into work early — so self-effacing that frequently the studio guards would harass him for identification. Who cared about songwriters in Hollywood? Certainly not the fans: when Harry rolled up at a premiere fans peered into his car and then informed the gang "It's nobody!" Certainly not the studio big shots: lyricist Lew Brown once argued the merits of his song with a studio boss. This is the way the argument ended:

Boss: "You're wrong."
Brown: "Why am I wrong?"
Boss: "Because I'm sitting behind the desk and you're standing in front of it."

At his solitary piano Harry Warren wrote 200 songs for fifty films between 1932 and 1958. He's probably written more hits than anybody apart from Irving Berlin. For *Dames* (1934), he and Dubin came up with the haunting "I Only Have Eyes For You", with its chromatic counter-melody and catchy triplets. Dubin, ever the warm-hearted sentimentalist, pictures a lovelorn suitor blind to all except his girl. In the film sequence Dubin's poem is set by Berkeley in a subway, which gives way to a dream of Ruby Keeler as a jigsaw puzzle, each bit held by a chorus girl. The song is repeated several times and this screen plugging helped sell it all over the world.

For "About A Quarter To Nine" Dubin and Warren had the help of ace song-salesman Al Jolson. Dressed in evening clothes he radiated the song to his wife Ruby Keeler in *Go Into Your Dance*. At the end they both smiled up to the moon, whose face was made up of girlie faces. Warren's melody is delightfully twisty and has a middle of tasty changes. He always dug hard for a different middle eight bars.

"Heavenly," said the *New Yorker* about MGM's *The Wizard of Oz* (1939). Warner's musicals had plenty of dash, zip and snappy urban slang, but MGM's quality was timelessness. Even Real Artists were attracted: MGM's Arthur Freed had his picture taken by Man Ray. "Over The Rainbow" from the score of *Oz* won an Academy Award for composer Harold Arlen and writer E.Y. Harburg. Hollywood must have straightened out Arlen. In the East he was known as a composer of bluesy songs for the "cream of sepia talent" at Harlem's Cotton Club. "He's the Negroist white man I ever knew," praised Ethel Waters. He wrote songs of more than thirty-two bars. But "Rainbow" is nice and regular, almost nursery comfortable. I mean, it's very good.

There was a terrific battle to get the song into the picture, though. Arlen felt the score needed a long, dreamy melody to offset the bouncy songs like "We're Off To See The Wizard". It came to him near Schwab's pharmacy on Sunset Boulevard while he was taking a spin in his car. Next day he complied with a middle eight, using that beloved see-saw phrase we heard in "Carolina in The Morning" and "My Buddy" and, of course, lots of other songs. Lyricist Harburg thought the tune was "too grand" and not right for a little Kansas girl. Ira Gershwin said it was good. Eventually words were married to music and taken to the MGM people, who said it dragged the picture. Three times "Rainbow" was chopped from *Oz* and three times songwriter/musical director Arthur Freed put it back in. Finally the song was left in — and of course, the rest is film history. Eventually it became identified with Judy Garland and even seemed to speak of her life's goal, an exchange of Klieg light for rainbowland. The last line is a good example of tempting pop logic: "If happy little bluebirds fly beyond the rainbow, why oh why can't I?"

Husband and wife team Al Jolson and Ruby Keeler star-gazing
during "A Quarter To Nine" routine in *Go Into Your Dance*
(Warner Bros First National, 1935). *Kobal Collection*

Paul Whiteman leading his orchestra in Universal's *King Of Jazz* (1930). Whiteman was responsible for raising the dance band to financial and artistic heights. He was also a kind and fair employer. *National Film Archive*

At The Moving Picture Ball

A Photo-Play In 2 Reels

Scenario by
HOWARD JOHNSON

Music by
JOS. SANTLY
Directed by Leo. Feist, Inc.

Tempo di Movie

Till ready

Reel 1. Hip hoo-ray__ I feel de-light-ed, Yes-ter-day__ I was in-vi-ted
Reel 2. Ev-'ry girl__ a hand-some look-er, Had a dance_ with Mis-ter Zu-kor

to a swell af-fair,____ All the mov-ie stars were there.____
Mis-ter Tho-mas Ince,____ Stepped a-round just like a prince.____

Oh what fun,_ the par-ty last-ed Till the break of dawn,
Wil-liam Fox,_ and Jes-sie Las-ky Both joined in the fun,

Fam-ous play-ers turned to ca-bar-et-ers, How they fooled and car-ried on.
Big di-rec-tors ming-led with the ac-tors, Why the whole bunch seemed like one.

2

CHARMAINE!

Tune 'Banjulele' Banjo & Ukulele thus:-

Bb Eb G C

*PIANO ACCORDION

Arrangement for 'Banjulele' Banjo & Ukulele by Alvin D. Keech.

by ERNO RAPEE
and
LEW POLLACK.

tears and cheers I heard you say, "CHAR-MAINE!" I

pre - cious mem - 'ry lin - gers yet, When you de -

Eb   Bbdim   Bb   G7   Cm

love you so.＿＿＿＿＿＿＿＿＿ Though old years turn to

clared your love.＿＿＿＿＿＿＿ And then you went a -

F9   Bb (dim Bb7 dim Bb)   Fm   C7

new,＿＿＿ My heart keeps call - ing you.＿＿＿ I

way,＿＿＿ And now each night and day.＿＿＿ I

rit.

Fm   G7   Cm   F7   Bb   Bb+

4

REFRAIN.

won - der   why   you   keep   me   wait   -   ing,   CHAR - MAINE___
won - der   why   you   keep   me   wait   -   ing,   CHAR - MAINE___

Eb   Eb maj7   Eb6

Eb

___ cries   in   vain,_____   I   won - der   when   blue - birds   are
___ my Char - maine_____   I   won - der   when   blue - birds   are

Bb dim   Bb7

mat   -   ing,   Will   you   come   back   a - gain,_____   I
mat   -   ing,   Will   you   come   back   a - gain,_____   I

Fm   Bb7   Bb+

Eb   Bb+

Featured in the 20th Century-Fox Picture "YOU WERE MEANT FOR ME"

You Were Meant For Me

Words by
ARTHUR FREED

Tune Ukulele
4 3 2 1
G C E A

See back page for
Introduction and Verse

Music by
NACIO HERB BROWN

CHORUS
Moderato

You were meant for me _____ I was

meant for you _____ Na - ture pat - terned you and

when she was done ___ You were all the sweet things

The letters below Bass Stave indicate names of Chords for Piano Accordion & Guitar

Rights authorised in Miller Music Corporation, New York

Copyright 1929, by Robbins Music Corporation, New York

FRANCIS, DAY & HUNTER, Ltd. 138-140, Charing Cross Rd. London. W.C.2.

F. & D. Ltd. 21804

4

INTRODUCTION and VERSE

Moderato

f

F

mp

Life was a song, You came a-long I've laid a-

F   F#dim   Gm   C7   F

- wake the whole night through   If I but dared

dim   Gm7   C7   E7   Gm   D7

To think you cared   This is what ___ I'd say to you

Back to Chorus

rall

Cdim   G7   Gm7   C7   E7

F. & D. Ltd. 21804.

Tip-toe thro' the Tulips with Me

Words by
AL DUBIN

Music by
JOE BURKE

Tune Guitar

E A D G B E

1. Shades of night are creep-ing   Wil-low trees are weep-ing,   Old folks and ba-bies are
2. Come on out and pet me   Come and "Ju-li-et" me,   Tease me and sly-ly "co-

sleep-ing;   Sil-ver stars are gleam-ing,   All a-lone I'm
-quette" me   Let me Ro-me-o you,   I just want to

schem-ing,   Schem-ing to get you out here,   my   dear, Come,
show you,   How much I'm will-ing to do   for   you, Come,

TIP-TOE THRO'

TIP-TOE THRO'

FELDMAN'S
40TH Song & Dance Album

COMPLETE WORDS & MUSIC
WITH TONIC SOL-FA SETTING,
UKULELE, GUITAR & PIANO-ACCORDION Ac

CONTENTS

DICK POWELL
in
WARNER BROS.
& VITAPHONE
PICTURE
"DAMES"

1/-
NET.
COPYRIGH

B. FELDMAN & CO.
125-9, SHAFTESBURY AVE.
LONDON W.C.2.

THIS BOOK MUST NOT BE EXPORTED TO CANADA
OR THE CONTINENTS OF EUROPE OR AUSTRALASIA

I ONLY HAVE EYES FOR YOU

Words by
AL DUBIN

Music by
HARRY WARREN

I only have eyes for you.

I only have eyes for you.

About A Quarter To Nine

Additional Lyrics by CHARLES DUNN
Ukulele arranged by R. S. STODDON
(The Letters below Bass Stave indicate names of Chords for Guitar and Piano Accordion)

From The First National Picture
"CASINO DE PAREE"

Words by
AL DUBIN

Music by
HARRY WARREN

....a-bout a quar-ter to nine............ My lov-in' arms .... are gon-na ten-der-ly twine..

A - round you,........... a-round a quar-ter to nine.... I know I

won't be late, 'cause at half-past eight I'm gon-na hur-ry there...... I'll be wait-ing where the lane be - gins,

wait-ing for you on nee-dles and pins. And then........... the world is gonna be mine,............ This

eve - ning,........... a-bout a quar-ter to nine......... The

poco rit. e dim.

D.C.

HENDERSON & SPALDING LTD
Music Engravers & Printers. London

About a quarter to nine

THE BEST IN THE WORLD

6d. EXTRA   [CONTINENTAL FINGERING]

OVER the RAINBOW

Words by — E·Y·HARBURG.   Music by· HAROLD ARLEN.

THE WIZARD OF "OZ"

with— JUDY GARLAND

FRANK MORGAN · · RAY BOLGER ·
BERT LAHR · JACK HALEY · BILLY BURKE

Directed by VICTOR FLEMING ·
A Metro-Goldwyn-Mayer Picture
Produced by MERVYN-LE-ROY

OVER THE RAINBOW...	1/-
THE MERRY OLD LAND OF OZ... ...	1/-
WE'RE OFF TO SEE THE WIZARD...	1/-
IF I ONLY HAD A BRAIN	1/-
DING-DONG! THE WITCH IS DEAD...	1/-
THE JITTERBUG...	1/-
SELECTION	2/6

1/-
Net.

LONDON.
FRANCIS, DAY & HUNTER Lᵀᴰ
138-140, Charing Cross Road. W.C.2.

NEW YORK.
LEO. FEIST, INC.
1629, BROADWAY.

Authorised for sale in The British Empire, exclusive of
Canada, Newfoundland & Australasia but not elsewhere.

Featured in the Metro-Goldwyn-Mayer Picture "WIZARD OF OZ"

Over The Rainbow

Words by
E. Y. HARBURG

Music by
HAROLD ARLEN

-by.	Some-where O-ver The Rain-bow skies are	blue,	And the	dreams that you dare to

dream real-ly do come true.	Some-day I'll wish up-on a star and wake up where the clouds are far be-hind	me.	Where

troub les melt like lem on drops, a-way, a bove the chim ney tops that's where you'll	find	me.	Some-where	O-ver The Rain-bow blue-birds

fly.	Birds	fly O-ver The Rain-bow, why then, oh why can't I?	I?

If hap py lit-tle blue birds fly be-yond the rain-bow, why oh why can't I?

Made in England

"These Yank songs are no more than the lugubrious lamentations of a disappointed lover," roared English songwriter Ralph Butler, a specialist in outdoor jollities like "I'm Happy When I'm Hiking". Nevertheless, American songs, especially picture songs, dominated the British market. Dance bands and crooners filled the music halls of the late twenties and the thirties. Few native singers stuck to their own accents (exceptions were Gracie Fields, George Formby and Vera Lynn) and few native songwriters made a dent in America (exceptions were Ray Noble, Kennedy and Carr, and Campbell and Connelly). As far as pop music was concerned, Britain was Little America.

"Having a whale of a time on the cruise. Giggle water every night at the captain's table. Not like grim old strike-ridden England!" wrote Tommy "Chin-chin" Winterbourne from aboard the S.S. *Gadfly* in 1931. "Dancing cheek to cheek to a top-hole band that, for a change, doesn't play in-out jizzy-jazz but foreign melodies. Especially a Spanish thing about a lady in Spain." But at the same time Reginald Buttersley of Coventry was noting in his exercise book, entitled *Wireless Log*, "Jack Payne and his Band have now performed "Lady of Spain" some fifty-seven times in the last six months. Is this a record?" No champagne for Buttersley, in trams but out-of-work — a piping hot water drink instead.

"Lady of Spain" (1931) was one of Britain's few whopping great world hits — everywhere but Spain, in fact. Tolchard Evans, Stanley Damerell and Bob Hargreaves* wrote it as part of their campaign to counter the Americans. Composer Evans, no lover of jizzy-jazz, had earlier come up with "Sunset Down In Somerset" and "Dreamy Devon" to tackle the Carolinas and Swanees. Songs had to be different, had to be novelties. So he wrote a paso doble in the form of the old Spanish "El Relicario". The verse was excellent but tricky. How the devil was he to get from the key of E flat to D major for the simple singalong chorus? The job took two weeks, and then Stanley Damerell and Bob Hargreaves had a hard time fitting in the words — but Stanley had at least got Walker's rhyming dictionary. The main tune was straight down the line and could be either a paso doble or a waltz, embellished or unembellished. Butcher boys could deal with it. Jack Payne and the BBC Dance Band were the first to take up "Lady Of Spain" and requests poured in at once. But the novelty pop is a difficult business. The follow-up had to be way-out, too. At least they succeeded with "Let's All Sing Like The Birdies Sing", a Germanic oom-pah waltz. Then Stanley went and wrote "I've Never Wronged An Onion — So Why Should it Make Me Cry?"

*On the song credit, the lyricists have boiled their names down to the pseudonym "Erell Reaves."

Whooping it up in their own way, British ballroom dancers pause for a pose on the parquet at the Empress Hall, Wigan (1939) — dancing from 7.30 p.m. to 9.30 p.m., admission 6d. *Radio Times Hulton Picture Library*

Farmyard antics had provided source material for not a few songs during the ragtime years. One thinks of "King Chanticleer" and "Down On The Farm". In Britain ragtime lingered longer by merging into musical hall comedy songs, notably those of George Formby. Leslie Sarony wrote about "Jollity Farm" and Ralph Butler of "Misery Farm". Butler actually owned a chicken farm, but the chickens he gave to his friends were always mysteriously wrapped in grocer's paper. In an age of show-biz sophistication — cocktails for two and dinner for one, please, James — it was refreshing to find these rustic songs. "Farmyard Cabaret" goes at a very infectious jog-trot and tells how the animals got stewed on cider. Albert Whelan recorded a very raggy version accompanied by Harry Hudson's Melody Men (British recording was acknowledged to be of much higher fidelity than American). I'm afraid the song was no hit, though.

British films were struggling, too, at this time. They were the laughing stock of the English-speaking world. Probably because they lacked Hollywood expertise and American accents. But at least the British quota system resulted in music hall stalwarts being preserved on film: Gus Elen, Florrie Forde, Charles Coborn, George Robey, Lily Morris were filmed statically but that's just as well. No Hollywood trickery. Gracie Fields from Lancashire saved British cinema from bankcruptcy. Some found her presence brazen and a threat to all that was cultured and gracious — like assault by flying fish and chips. But millions of ordinary folk flocked to see Our Gracie being cheeky to the toffs and an inspiration to the workers in such films as *Sally In Our Alley* and *Sing As We Go*.

"Sally", the song that became Gracie Fields's signature tune, was in her first film

Gracie Fields, Britain's No. 1 star, milks a cow for the first time in her life during farmyard scene in *Keep Smiling* (1938). Unlike so many of her singing contemporaries she remained, in her art, British to the core. *Kobal Collection*

Sally In Our Alley (1931). Nobody connected with the production thought the song would catch on. After all, here was Gracie singing a man's song. Still, she was pretty good at tackling any material and in the "Sally" sequence she pulled funny faces when the words got a big sentimental. Leo Towers and Harry Leon, two writers who haunted Denmark Street in search of crisp oncers or even fivers, originated "Sally". When they approached publisher Bill Haines the song was called "Gypsy Sweetheart", which Bill changed to "Mary" and then to "Sally". An old pal, blotto and passing through, supplied "beguiling" to rhyme with "smiling". An associate of Gracie's suggested "You're more than the whole world to me". And the idea of a Sally in an alley was well established in the world of popular music: "I Wonder What's Become Of Sally?" and "Sally (You Brought The Sunshine To Our Alley")". In such a manner of cooperation were songs knitted together in those days.

Denmark Street and environs was Britain's Tin Pan Alley, and one day, in the thirties, an Austrian composer of classical music came knocking. Will Grosz, who had conducted the Berlin Philharmonic and arranged Strauss for ten pianos, was Jewish and had had to flee Hitler's Germany. With his wife and a suitcase he now came to Denmark Street with some melodies. Bert Feldman, the publisher, teamed him with Jimmy Kennedy, graduate of Trinity College, Dublin, and specialist in writing new words to continental numbers. Feldman didn't like their first effort so they took it to Jimmy Phillips at Peter Maurice Music. "You can't have linden trees in a lyric today," said Jimmy Phillips. "And Germany's not too popular. How about walnut trees?" The song was re-set in Capri, and as "The Isle of Capri" it set off to fame, pushed hard by Lew Stone and his Band.

Native melody makers. *Wildcroft Pix*

Will Grosz's royalties were automatically going to Austria, so Phillips arranged for him to have a nom de plume. The Austrian was heavily-built and was a William, so Hugh (Huge) Williams seemed a natural. "Leaving aside your classical stuff, have you got any more of these folk tunes?" asked Phillips. Kennedy and Williams produced "Red Sails In The Sunset" (inspired by an Irish sunset), "Poor Little Angeline" (which inspired the Palais Glide dance step) and "Harbour Lights", among others.

"Harbour Lights" (1937) has topped the best-selling record lists three times: by Rudy Vallee in 1937, by Sammy Kaye in 1950 and by The Platters in 1958. Throughout John Ford's film *The Long Voyage Home* the tune was spun movingly. A very folksy tune, smacking of slow salty rollers. Kennedy got the title from a pub called "Harbour Lights", which he came upon one night when he got lost driving home to Weybridge from Portsmouth.

Kennedy wrote a bunch of hits with the irrepressible Michael Carr, son of "Cockney" Cohen, the bookmaker and boxing champion. Carr, who liked to affect an American accent by talking out of the side of his mouth, was always in a hurry to get a song finished so he could "collect" from the publisher and then hit the night-clubs. Kennedy was a home person and steady, but nevertheless the two sparked off some smashes: "South Of The Border", "Home Town" and "The Washing On The Siegfried Line".

Kennedy originally made up the "Siegfried" song in 1939 for the entertainment of his Territorial Army troop, but the canny Carr rushed it on to the air in Bristol. The popular comedy team of Flanagan and Allen took up the song and soon troops all over Britain were singing "Siegfried". The Ministry of Information spotted a grand morale-booster and made sure copies of the song were smuggled into neutral countries. Hitler was as enraged as he had been by the German success of "Yes, We Have No Bananas". Then came the fall of France and Dunkirk. The Nazis threatened Britain with invasion. "Siegfried Line" died a natural death. Gleefully Lord Haw-Haw, in propaganda broadcasts from Berlin, seized on the unfortunate song to sneer and condemn as "stinking fish".

The Nazis twisted their knife in the wound. The Kennedy-Carr song was re-recorded by the enemy and wickedly parodied. First we hear a group of Tommies singing the chorus, terrific explosions, then Nazi Youths take up the chorus but in German, with new aggressive lyrics. This version was played relentlessly over the radio in every occupied country. Came 1945 and the defeat of Germany. As the Tommies marched into the liberated countries, they were greeted by native choruses of "Siegfried Line", back in its original words!

Jimmy Kennedy, graduate of Trinity College, Dublin, and Tin Pan Alley (G.B.), accompanies group of cheery soldiers in a chorus of "We're Gonna Hang Out The Washing On The Siegfried Line" during the Phoney War. *E.M.I. Publishing*

Lady of Spain

Sensational Dance Rage of London and Paris

Words by
Erell Reaves
Music by
Tolchard Evans

Agnes
1-14-32

SAM FOX PUB. CO.
CLEVELAND · NEW YORK
LONDON · PARIS · BERLIN · MELBOURNE
ESTABLISHED THROUGHOUT THE WORLD

LADY OF SPAIN

Copyright 1931 by Cecil Lennox Ltd.
Copyright assigned 1940 to Fred Hartley Publications Ltd., for the British Empire (excluding Canada and Australasia)
Copyright assigned 1944 to The Peter Maurice Music Co. Ltd., Maurice Building, Denmark St. London. W.C.2.
for the entire world.
Telegrams: Mauritunes Westcent London.

Telephone: Temple Bar 3856

3

CHORUS

LA - DY OF SPAIN, I a - dore you

Right from the night I first saw you,

My heart has been yearn - ing for you,

What else could an - y heart do?

THE FARMYARD CABARET

ALBERT WHELAN

WITH HARRY HUDSON MELODY MEN

Featured on Panachord Records

THE FARMYARD CABARET

Tune Ukulele to F.Bb.D.G.

ROY LESLIE &
CLAY KEYES.

Copyright MCMXXXII, for all Countries by Campbell, Connelly & Co. Ltd. 11, Denmark St. London. W.C.2.

C.C P.688.

CHORUS.

The cocks all start a-crowing, The hors-es shout "Hey-hey." As the old blue pig does an I-rish jig, At the
The hors-es start a-crowing, The cocks be-gin to neigh, When the corn fed cow says, "Me-ow-ow-ow," At the

Farm-yard Ca-ba-ret......... The tur-key does the tan-go, The don-key starts to bray, When they dance John Peel and the
Farm-yard Ca-ba-ret......... The don-key starts a-moo-ing, Which makes the old bull say, "You can try to moo but they

Chick-en Reel, At the Farm-yard Ca-ba-ret. The poor old house-dog, Ro-ver, goes wob-bley at the joints, The
can't milk you," At the Farm-yard Ca-ba-ret. The poor old house-dog, Ro-ver, says bark-ing ain't no joke, The

por-cu-pines in clo-ver, he's show-ing off his points, When the rab-bits do the Rhum-ba, The
frog shouts, "I'll come o-ver and teach you how to croak." Then the ducks, and geese and chick-ens, Give a

hens all shout "Hoo-ray!" And the bum-ble bee's gon-na sting 'em free, At the Farm-yard Ca-ba-ret......... The -ret....
loud Hip-hip-hoo-ray! When the old blue pig lays an egg that big, At the Farm-yard Ca-ba-ret......... The -ret.

D.S.

Sally
by
WILL E. HAINES
HARRY LEON &
LEO TOWERS.
Theme Song to the
Talking-Singing Film
SALLY IN OUR ALLEY
AN ASSOCIATED RADIO
PICTURE
Distributed by
RADIO PICTURES LTD
Featuring
GRACIE
FIELDS
6D.
KEITH PROWSE & Co. LTD.

2

GRACIE FIELDS great Song Success in the film "SALLY IN OUR ALLEY"

SALLY

Tune Uke:-

* ACCORDION

Words and Music by
WILL E. HAINES
HARRY LEON & LEO TOWERS

4255b

3

Chorus (Con espressione)

K. P. & Co. Ltd. 4255b

4

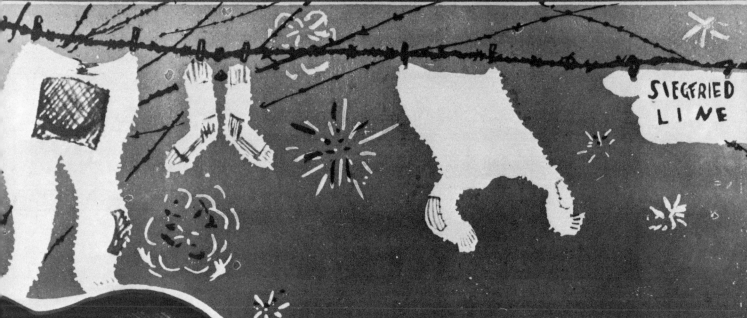

CHORUS

WE'RE GONNA HANG OUT THE WASH-ING ON THE SIEG-FRIED LINE Have you a-ny dir-ty wash-ing mo-ther

dear?_____ WE'RE GON-NA HANG OUT THE WASH-ING ON THE SIEG-FRIED LINE 'Cos the wash-ing

day is here_____ Wheth-er the weath-er may be wet or fine We'll just

rub a-long with-out a care_____ WE'RE GON-NA HANG OUT THE WASHING ON THE SIEG-FRIED

LINE If the Sieg-fried Line's still there. WE'RE GON-NA there._____

We're gonna hang out the washing

RED SAILS IN THE SUNSET

MUSIC:
HUGH WILLIAMS

LYRICS:
JIMMY KENNEDY

6 D NET

Featured by
LEW STONE
AND HIS BAND

The PETER MAURICE MUSIC CO. LTD.

RED SAILS IN THE SUNSET

Tune Ukulele: A D F# B

* Accordeon

Written & Composed by
JIMMY KENNEDY
& HUGH WILLIAMS

Slow

Piano

mp

KEY G

'Twas down where fish-er folk gath-er, I wan-der'd far from the throng. I
Red Sails the night breeze is blow-ing, And clouds are hid-ing the moon A-

Accordeon * G   F 9th

heard a fish-er girl sing-ing And this re-frain was her song.
bove no bright stars are glow-ing It means the storms com-ing soon.

G   C   Cmi   G   A7   C   D7

Chorus

RED SAILS IN THE SUNSET ___   'Way out on the sea   Oh, carry my lov'd one ___

G   G7   C   Cmi   G   G   Ddim   C   D7

Copyright MCMXXXV in all Countries by

THE PETER MAURICE MUSIC Co. Ltd.

Telephone: Temple Bar 3856 (5 lines)   Maurice Building, Denmark St., London, W.C.2   Telegrams: "Maurilunes Westcent London"

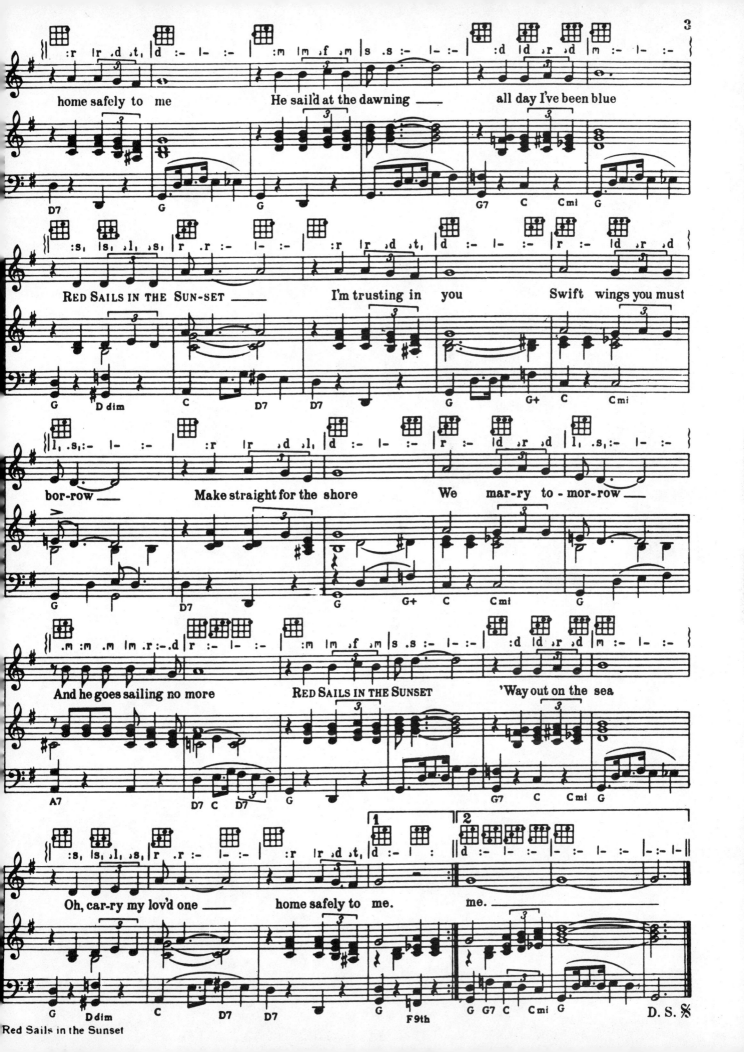

Red Sails in the Sunset

Harbour Lights

TANGO - FOXTROT BALLAD

6D NET

WORDS AND MUSIC BY:
JIMMY KENNEDY
AND
HUGH WILLIAMS

HARBOUR LIGHTS

Words and Music by JIMMY KENNEDY and HUGH WILLIAMS

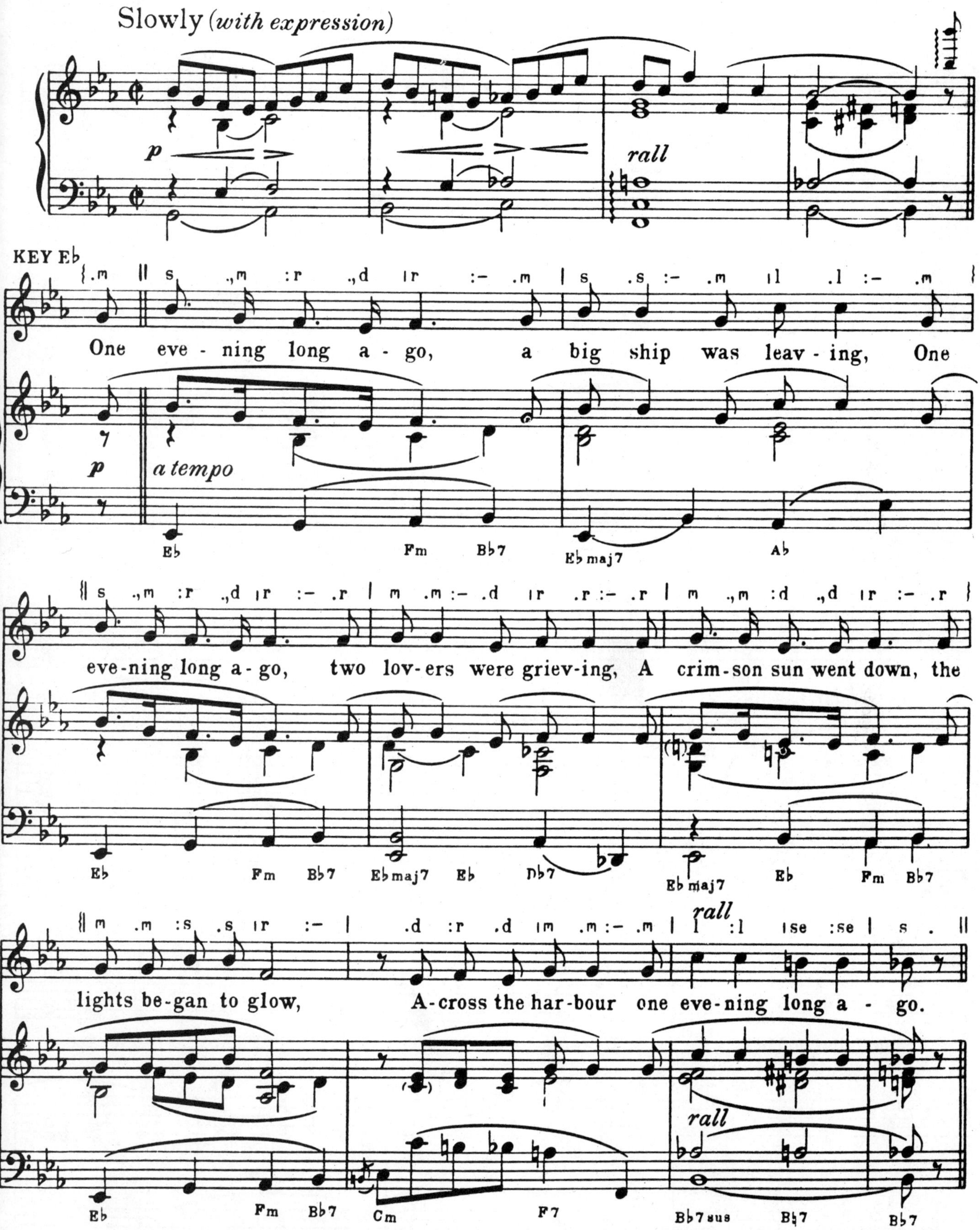
Slowly (with expression)
p
rall
KEY E♭
a tempo
One eve - ning long a - go, a big ship was leav - ing, One
eve-ning long a - go, two lov-ers were griev-ing, A crim-son sun went down, the
lights be-gan to glow, A-cross the har-bour one eve-ning long a - go.
E♭ Fm B♭7 E♭maj7 A♭
E♭ Fm B♭7 E♭maj7 E♭ D♭7 E♭maj7 E♭ Fm B♭7
E♭ Fm B♭7 Cm F7 B♭7sus B♭7 B♭7

2

CHORUS *(Slowly with expression)*

I saw the Har - bour Lights, They on-ly told me we were part - ing, The same old

Har - bour Lights, That once brought you to me. I watched the

Har - bour Lights, How could I help if tears were start - ing? Good-bye to

ten - der nights, Be-side the sil - v'ry sea. I longed to

On the Continent

Before Beethoven, I'm told, "serious" composers wrote popular songs. Mozart, for example, was whistled on the street and would, in turn, stick a few current hits into his operas. But Beethoven started the split between art music and pop music. No longer was the music man a public servant but high priest of his own soul, answerable only to God.

Austria, Germany, France, Italy and other European countries had their own popular music trade in the nineteenth century, but in the twentieth the Continent welcomed with open arms the American musical invaders. First ragtime and cakewalks; then jazz and the charleston. Afro-American folk music was new; European folk music was traditional, unchanging. You wore funny costumes, quaint and archaic, to sing and dance in the Alpine manner. You wore normal clothes, flannels and a blazer and maybe color-coordinated two-tone shoes, to sing and dance the latest American numbers.

Europe, leaderless and without any dynamic new music, fell to the Yankee with his spicy music and super salesmanship. However, people cannot exist with just spice and beat. As we've seen, they need languorous love songs, and European composers were first class at writing these. After all, romance — the dark forest, flaxen-haired maiden, tall blond knight — originated in Europe. And surely Santa Claus came from Germany?

After the Great War one of the first American dance bands to tour Europe was Paul Whiteman's His pretentions always leaned slightly towards the quasi-classical, and so he welcomed a new piece of material presented to him in Vienna which had long lines and high yearning. *Madonna, Du Bist Schoner Als Der Sonnenschein!* by Dr Robert Katscher was the hit of the 1924 revue *Kusse Um Mitternacht.* In America the Whiteman band made a full-throated recording of the tune complete with symphonic verse followed by hot chorus, featuring Henry Busse's squeezing horn. Buddy De Sylva put some twilight words to the tune and off it went to become a standard. "When Day Is Done" (1926), is one of my favorite songs. It was played at Paul Whiteman's funeral.

Middle Europe has contributed much culturally to America. I would go as far as to say that many Americans are physically very Germanic. Then there's the Prussian haircut or crewcut (now disappearing in the U.S.), the team spirit, the hamburger and frankfurter, the pursuit of hygiene. There are still polka programs on local TV in America. Germans, Austrians, Poles, Bohemians, Serbo-Croats, all formed their own little worlds in America, retaining old-world ways. In 1939 a Czechoslovakian polka song originally titled "Skoda Lasky" became a

JACK HYLTON PLAYS TO VAST AUDIENCES AT LEIPZIG. ——— *Remarkable Photograph.*

RHYTHM. December, 1932

"What wouldn't I do for that man?": Aryan night-clubbers stepping out to dance band in Hitler's pre-war Germany. *Bettmann Archive*

smash record as "Beer Barrel Polka" sung by the bubbly harmony group the Andrews Sisters. It had reached America in a recording by Will Glahe and his Musette Orchestra, and had earlier passed through Britain (in 1936) when Jimmy Kennedy was invited to write an English lyric by his publishers. At the time he was a bit fed up with fitting English words to Continental melodies so he dropped the song. America's Lew Brown eventually put the present back-slapping lyric to "Beer Barrel Polka". In England the song became known as "Roll Out The Barrel" and was enthusiastically adopted by pub carousers as their theme tune. Washerwomen and fish-ladies would perform creditable "knees-ups" and "slap thighs" to the Barrel polka at closing time. During World War II the song was a favorite of soldiers and sailors, and was often heard as ships went down.

But the real theme song of World War II was "Lili Marlene", a favorite of both Allies and Germans. The words go back to the Great War when Hans Leip, a German soldier about to join battle on the Russian Front, wrote a poem called 'Lili Marlene" — combining the name of his girl with that of his pal's girl.

In the late thirties Lale Andersen, popular with the student crowd at late-night Munich and Berlin cabarets, found the poem in a book and had a friend write a tune. This tune was rather duff and it was Norbert ("Bombs on England") Schultze who eventually wrote the final melody. Lale Andersen's recording was issued in 1939 on Electrola.

Came the Second World War and the North African campaign. A disc jockey at a radio station run by German propaganda experts in Belgrade stuck with very few records, came upon a record of "Lili Marlene" by Lale Andersen on Italian HMV. He spun and spun and spun it. Desert radios picked up the number.

We switch now to England in the war, to a pub in Stoke Poges. Publisher Jimmy Phillips is having a game of darts with bandleader Billy Cotton when in bursts a bunch of boisterous soldiers, and almost immediately they break into "Lili Marlene" — in German. Just for a joke Jimmy Phillips says "Better be careful with that song, boys, or we'll have the village copper here arresting you as enemy spies". Their officer approaches Jimmy and, rather close, says through clenched teeth, "Look here, this is our song! This is the song we hear on our radios in our tanks in the North African desert. This is the song we hear the German prisoners sing as their long snake-line winds its way through the sand storm to our headquarters. Mouth organs strike up "Lili" at night. We sing it in day-charges against the Germans. "Lily Marlene" gets us right in our guts. "Lili Marlene" is the theme song of the desert war and get that straight!" Quick as a wink Jimmy says, "Why don't you get some English lyrics then?" The officer sings him six English versions but Jimmy finds they all stink.

Back in London, Jimmy Phillips discovered the origins of "Lili" and also learned that permission had to be obtained from the Custodian of Enemy Copyrights before any new version was made of the song. This was obtained with the blessing of the Ministry of Information which had cottoned on to the success of the song among British troops and was keen to get a decent British version out on the double. Jimmy and lyricist Tommie Connor brought the German poem down to earth. "As far as I could see," says Jimmy, "the German song was about a barracks tart that this soldier dreams about. He sees her coming down to him in the trenches enveloped in a regular lust cloud. All that's a bit poetic, so we put in some lamplight scenes and made the song more accessible." Billy Cotton made a record, Anne Shelton had a hit record, but it was Marlene Dietrich who became "Lili" in American concerts. Not until 1958 were the royalties paid to the German company, because the war took a long time clearing up.

America's own Lili Marlene: movie actress Marlene Dietrich is given rousing reception by battle veterans on the *Monticello*, after ship docked in New York (July 20th, 1945). *Kobal Collection*

When Day Is Done

Words by
B. G. DE SYLVA.

Music by
ROBERT KATSCHER.

3

From the mo - ment you came.
At the edge of the sky.

ev - 'ry day's a grey day since you left my sight,
Work is done, and grey life is like a song to me,

And the love - li - ness of the night
For some trea - sures be - long to me

Is no long - er the same.
That no mo - ney can buy.

When

When day is done

4

REFRAIN. *dreamily*

day is done and shad-ows fall I dream of you; When

day is done I think of all the joys we knew. That

yearn-ing re-turn-ing To hold you in my arms Won't go, love, I

know, love. With-out you night has lost its charms! When day is done and

When day is done

479

Beer Barrel Polka
(ROLL OUT THE BARREL)

BEAR BRAND RANCH
SAN JUAN CAPISTRANO, CAL.

Blue Barron
and his Orchestra

By LEW BROWN,
WLADIMIR A. TIMM
and JAROMIR VEJVODA

SHAPIRO, BERNSTEIN & Co. Inc.
MUSIC PUBLISHERS   NEW YORK

MADE IN U.S.A.

IM·HO
F.R.

ROLL OUT THE BARREL
(BEER BARREL POLKA)

By LEW BROWN
WLADIMIR A. TIMM
& JAROMIR VEJVODA

3

5

LILLI MARLENE

(Pronounced "LILY MARLANE")

Words and Music by

HANS LEIP
NORBERT SCHULTZE
& TOMMIE CONNOR

Tune Uke G.C.E.A.
*Accordion

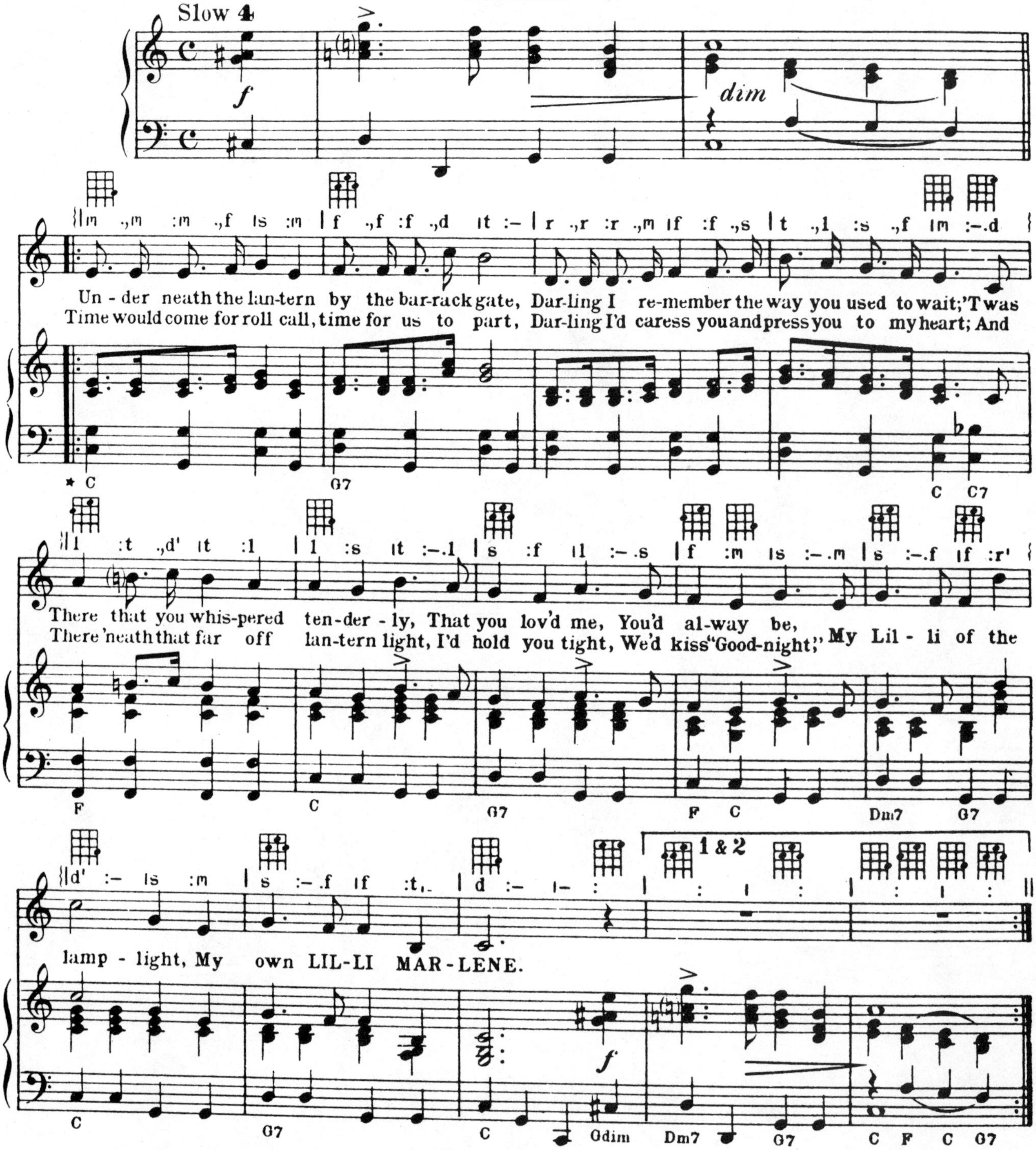

Slow 4
f
dim
Un - der neath the lan-tern by the bar-rack gate, Dar-ling I re-member the way you used to wait; 'Twas
Time would come for roll call, time for us to part, Dar-ling I'd caress you and press you to my heart; And
* C
G7
C C7
There that you whis-pered ten-der - ly, That you lov'd me, You'd al-way be,
There 'neath that far off lan-tern light, I'd hold you tight, We'd kiss "Good-night," My Lil - li of the
F
C
G7
F C
Dm7 G7
lamp - light, My own LIL-LI MAR-LENE.
1 & 2
f
C
G7
C
Gdim
Dm7
G7
C F C G7

Lilli Marlene

Biographies of composers

Alleyman meets Pallyman: veteran songwriter Bud Green with the Duke of Edinburgh at a 1970s London reception. *Bud Green*

FRED AHLERT
(1892-1953) Started as arranger to Waterson, Berlin and Synyder Co. Special knowledge of law invaluable during his presidency of ASCAP. Handful of hits, mostly with words by Roy Turk: 'I'll Get By', 'Mean To Me', 'Where The Blue Of The Night Meets The Gold Of The Day', 'I'm Gonna Sit Right Down And Write Myself A Letter'.

FELIX BERNARD
(1897-1944) Composer from Brooklyn. Professional pianist from childhood. Active in vaudeville, later played for dance bands. Wrote special material for stars like Sophie Tucker, Al Jolson, Eddie Cantor. Hits: 'Dardanella', 'Winter Wonderland'.

JOHNNY BLACK
(Dates unknown) Obscure songwriter and ragtime pianist. Shotgun marriage to Felix ('Dardanella') Bernard. Seen around publishing offices in 1920's with self-penned potential hits. Died sometime in the 1930's or early 1940's.

HAROLD ARLEN
(1905-) Cantor's son, synagogue choirboy — hence Yiddishe-blues turn of melody? Wrote Cotten Club specialties, then Broadway and Hollywood. In-trade fave: smoothly wailing singer too: 'Between The Devil And The Deep Blue Sea', 'Stormy Weather', 'The Man That Got Away', Over The Rainbow ', etc.

NACIO HERB BROWN
(1896-1964) West coast man, never in Alley. From rag trading and real estate into occasional song hits (twenties novelette 'Doll Dance'). MGM boy-genius Irving Thalberg coaxed Brown into fulltime writing, starting with *Broadway Melody* score: 'You Were Meant For Me', 'Wedding Of The Painted Doll' plus title song. Adept at classy nursery tunes, instantly hummable: 'Singing In The Rain', 'Pagan Love Song', 'All I Do Is Dream Of You', 'You Are My Lucky Star', All the words by Arthur Freed.

JOE BURKE
(1884-1950) Although a few alley hits ('Carolina Moon', 'Baby Your Moth Mother'), he found gold in Hollywood musicals like *Gold Diggers Of Broadway* ('Tip-toe Through The Tulips', 'Painting The Clouds With Sunshine'). One of his biggest songs was cut from its original film score and later rose from Alley, 'I'm Dancing With Tears In My Eyes'. As usual, the movie moguls had no idea about what was wanted in pop music. Still today they see life through celluloid.

MICHAEL CARR
(1905-68) Real name Michael Cohen. Son of boxing champ, 'Cockney' Cohen. Raised in Dublin, ran away to U.S.A. and roughed it. In 1929 became Soho waiter. From 1930 was songwriter, initially working on Gracie Fields vehicles. Changed name from Cohen to Carr in 1933. Wrote 'Old Faithful' with Jimmy Kennedy's brother. Big U.S. hit. With Jimmy Kennedy he wrote three Palladium scores and six film musicals including an Ambrose, and Arthur Tracy and a Flanagan and Allen. Hits include: 'Dinner For One Please, James', 'The Rhythm's O.K. in Harlem', 'On The Outside Looking In', 'White Horses', 'The Washing On the Siegfied Line'.

HARRY CARROLL
(1892-1962) Silent movie-theater pianist and cafe entertainer before becoming Alley arranger. Contracted to Shubert Bros, Broadway impresarios, as revue songwriter. Also on vaude stage as act. After death of vaude he took to night-clubs. Hits: 'On The Mississippi' (outstanding rag song), 'Trail Of The Lonesome Pine' (deathless nature song, recorded umpteen times — nice versions by Laurel and Hardy, Goldie Hawn), 'By the Beautiful Sea' (later used as TV suntan lotion jingle), 'Down in Bom-Bombay' (way ahead of its time), 'I'm Always Chasing Rainbows'.

ZEZ CONFREY
(1895-   ) Specialist in syncopated firework piano novelettes, the glossy end of the ragtime tradition. In "His tricky (and at times tricksy) piano style, the goal of many a collegiate, was bared on paper in his textbook bestseller *Zez Confrey's Modern Course in Novelty Piano Playing*. Began as vaude band drummer. Gained vital experience as roll cutter for piano rolls — a shattering art with over-dub capabilities, not yet fully appraised and praised. Wrote 'Stumbling'. Novelettes: 'Kitten On The Keys', 'Dizzy Fingers'. Mini-opera: *Thanksgiving*.

NOEL COWARD
(1899-1973) Composer, lyricist, author, playwright, film director, night-club entertainer. Almost low-born, he came to personify the upper-crust, seen-and-done-it-all gadfly to the punter millions. A real professional, fast worker, master of pastiche. The light touch belonged to a deeply conservative mind, harking back to the certainties of Edwardian life: *Cavalcade* charted the road to decadence trod by the British people. World War II brought classes together again temporarily *(In Which We Serve)*, pyramid-style. Coward spoke for the upper-middle classes, a breed without artistic leaders today. Self-taught pianist, one-key man (E flat). Began as revue contributor and performer, went on to serious plays *(The Vortex)* operetta *(Bitter Sweet)* and even ballet *(London Morning)*. His songs are his real gems, best rendered by the Master himself, and ranging from tingling romanticism ('Someday I'll Find You') to high camp ('Matelot', 'I've Been To A Marvellous Party').

BUDDY DE SYLVA
(1895-1950) Composer, publisher and producer. Part of famous De Sylva Brown and Henderson writing team. Educated at University of Southern California, lured to New York and away from surfing life by Al Jolson after latter picked up De Sylva initial hit ' 'N Everything'. There followed Jolie-tailored numbers such as 'I'll Say She Does', 'You Ain't Heard Nothin' Yet', knock-'em -dead stuff. On to collaboration with Gus Kahn, George Gershwin, Jerome Kern, Richard Whiting, Vincent Youmans, Nacio Herb Brown. De Sylva, Brown and Henderson team formed in 1925 and turned out boffo Broadway fast-paced shows. To Hollywood for songwriting chores; then produced Shirley Temple pics and became Paramount exec. producer in forties. Biopic: *The Best Things In Life Are Free.* Played a neat ukulele.

WALTER DONALDSON
(1893-1947) Amazingly prolific. Domestic bliss songs a specialty, (but a hot ladies' man, they say). After early hits ('You'd Never Know That Old Home Town Of Mine'), he joined Irving Berlin's publishing company and stayed a decade. Wrote score of smash show *Whoopee,* Eddie Cantor vehicle, later filmed. To Hollywood to dress film scores. Died there at fifty-three. Among his smashes were 'How Ya Gonna Keep 'Em Down On The Farm?', 'My Mammy', 'My Buddy', 'Carolina in the Morning,' 'Yes Sir That's My Baby', 'I Wonder Where My Baby Is Tonight?', 'At Sundown', 'My Blue Heaven', 'Tain't No Sin', 'Little White Lies', 'You're Driving Me Crazy'., 'Love Me or Leave Me'. A past master at the ultra-simple adhesive melody but little success in tired thirties. A glutton for the sixth note.

DAN DOUGHERTY
(1897-1955) Irish-American tunesmith, best-known for his 'Glad Rag Doll' which he wrote with the famous team of Yellen and Ager for the 1929 talkie *The Glad Rag Doll.* Like Yellen and Ager he wrote special material for Sophie Tucker, the Red Hot Momma.

DAVE DREYER
(1894-   ) Skilled piano accompanist. Among his clients: Al Jolson, Sophie Tucker, Belle Baker. RKO Radio Pictures music chief during thirties. His hits made in twenties, though: 'Me And My Shadow', 'There's A Rainbow 'Round My Shoulder', 'Cecilia', 'Back In Your Own Back Yard', 'Golden Gate'.

TOLCHARD EVANS
(1901-   ) Stalwart hero of G.B. Alley, writing songs praising local beauty spots (e.g.: 'Sunset Down In Somerset', 'The Road To Loch Lomond') and gaining relief conducting weekend seaside light orchestra. Wrote good comedy tunes ('The Organ Grinder Grinds All Day') but found rich vein in ballads ('If', 'Unless', 'Faith') and particularly in foreign parts ('Lady Of Spain'). Special material for George Formby and Gracie Fields. Still around, lives in Willesden, vegetarian and full of droll tales.

FRED FIS(C)HER
(1875-1942) Exceptionally extravagant, colorful tune/ wordsmith and publisher; born in Germany, served in Imperial German Navy and French Foreign Legion before bursting into Alley at dawn of century. Retained thick guttural accent always but discarded the C in his name when America entered World War I. Coined canny phrase: "Zong writing iss a qvestion off zounds, not zense." Once threw heavy typewriter out of top floor skyscraper window for joke. Committed suicide by a similar method. A few of his many hits: 'Peg O' My Heart', 'Dardanella', 'Chicago', 'If The Man In The Moon Were a Coon', 'They Go Wild, Simply Wild, Over Me', 'Happy Days and Lonely Nights', 'Who Paid The Rent For Mrs Rip Van Winkle When Rip Van Winkle Went Away?'

GEORGE GERSHWIN

(1898-1937) Put pop on serious-music map during Jazz Age when his 'Rhapsody In Blue' was performed by Paul Whiteman wedding-cake full ork at famous Aeolian Hall, New York, 1924. Longhair critics divided but sheet score sold a million. Sense of mission for American music climaxed in opera *Porgy and Bess* (1935). Melodies characterized by flash rhythmic devices ('Fascinating' Rhythm') and cunning chord sequences ('The Man I Love'), scientific blue notes ('I'll Build a Stairway to Paradise') and All-American drive ('Swanee'). Great and showy pianist — Ravel's birthday wish was to hear him play. Hits include: 'Somebody Loves Me', 'Baby Be Good', 'Someone To Watch Over Me', ''S Wonderful', 'I Got Rhythm', 'But Not For Me', 'Summertime', 'A Foggy Day'. Most lyrics by literate brother Ira, pastmaster at slangy expressions. Shows include *Lady Be Good, Oh, Kay, Funny Face, Of Thee I Sing* (first musical to win Pulitzer Prize). Films include: *Shall We Dance, A Damsel In Distress* (story by P.G. Wodehouse). A fave of G.B. royalty.

WILL GROSZ

(1894-1939) Austrian-Jewish composer of modern classical music. Conducting experience with the Berlin Philharmonic. Left Germany after Hitler's rise and made home in England. Wrote most of his hit melodies to words by Jimmy Kennedy. Used pseudonym 'Hugh Williams' for certain songs. Hits: 'Isle of Capri', 'Poor Little Angeline', 'Harbour Lights', 'Red Sails in The Sunset'.

ROBERT KATSCHER

(1894-1942) Viennese Doctor of Music, wrote operettas there. Moved to U.S. in early 1930's, wrote film scores. Apart from 'When Day Is Done' (original Austrian title 'Madonna'.) the doctor had no other hits.

JIMMY KENNEDY

(1902-   ) Irish composer/wordsman, educated at my old alma mater, Trinity College, Dublin, Eire. (We produced an earlier hit writer in Percy ['Mountains of Mourne' 'Phil The Fluter's Ball'] French).

Slated for Colonial Civil Service job but opted for G.B. Alley job. Started with community sing-song stuff for Blackpool consumption ('The Barmaid's Song'). Position at Feldman's where specialized in English lyrics to Continental songs ('Oh Donna Clara') and oldies ('Blaze Away', 'Teddy Bears' Picnic') and second verses to imported U.S. songs. Teamed up by Feldman with Austrian refugee music doctor Will Grosz (Hugh Williams). Result: 'Isle of Capri', 'Red Sails in The Sunset', 'Harbour Lights'. Their 'Poor Little Angeline' became inspiration for palais glide dance-step when Glaswegian Palais de Dansers, unable to foxtrot to tune, linked arms and improvised high-kick perambulation. Kennedy's own 'Roll Along Covered Wagon' was first hillbilly hit by limey (featured in Richard Dix oater). With Michael Carr he wrote 'South Of The Border' which became world smash and title tune for Gene Autry oater, and also 'The Washing On The Siegried Line'. After World War II Kennedy worked in U.S. contributing award-winning 'The Red We Want Is The Red We've Got In The Old Red White and Blue' to anti-Communist movement. Temporarily retired by anti-romantic Beatle age, but now returning with light instrumentals.

BILLY MAYHEW

(1889-1951) One-hit sole writer of 'It's A Sin To Tell A Lie'.

NEIL MORET

(1878-1943) Real name was Charles N. Daniels. Mid-westerner whose early work in Missouri, cradle of classic prairie ragtime, included arranging Scott Joplin's first published rag 'Original Rags'. After staff job at Remick's he founded own firm and moved to San Francisco. Early hits embraced pseudo-Indian intermezzos 'Hiawatha' and 'Silver Heels', and barbershop classic 'You Tell Me Your Dream, I'll Tell You Mine'. Wrote one of the first movie screen songs in *Mickey*, used in 1918 tie-up with Mabel Normand' vehicle of same name. In twenties he came up with 'Chloe' and the Chopin-inspired 'Moonlight And Roses'.

ERNO RAPEE

(1891-1945) Distinguished Hungarian conductor of grand opera before emigration to U.S. In charge of N.Y. symphony ork for silent movie-theater, then NBC Radio music director and head music man at Radio City Music Hall. Apart from 'Charmaine' theme song he also had hit with 'Diane', another movie theme *(Seventh Heaven)*.

RICHARD RODGERS
1902-   ) Well-educated at
Columbia U, cut above average
Alleyman. Smart varsity show
scores, with lyrics
by perfectionist
phrase-tickler Lorenz Hart,
spurned by TPA initially, until
clicking of shoestring-budgeted
arts-and-craft-originated
Garrick Gaieties revue
('Manhattan'). Rodgers and
Hart team followed up with
series of impeccable show
and film hits, characterized by
a happy mixture of rather
romantic melodies and
preciously clever lyrics.
Rogers, it seems was ever
the dutiful craftsman keeping
a clockwork schedule whilst
Hart led a madly bohemian
existence, disappearing into
another dark life for days on
end. Though they jeweled
their songs they were for hire
in the market place ('Ten Cents a
Dance' was written to order in
a few minutes). Song partnership
was longest in pop history —
over twenty-four years — and
broke up in 1943 as a result
of professional differences.
Oscar Hammerstein II, an
old friend, took over the lyric
chores producing pleasing and
fangless poems. The bite went
out but the money kept
coming in, and some really
lovely songs were made (e.g.:
'If I Loved You'). Just a cluster
of Rodgers and Hart hits:
'The Blue Room', 'Mountain
Greenery', 'Thou Swell',
'You Took Advantage Of Me',
'With A Song In My Heart',
'Dancing On The Ceiling',
'Isn't It Romantic?' 'Lover'
'There's a Small Hotel', 'Glad
To Be Unhappy', 'My Funny
Valentine', 'The Lady Is A
Tramp', 'Bewitched,
Bothered And Bewildered',
'Blue Moon'.

VINCENT ROSE
(1880-1944) Italian-born
pianist/violinist /ork leader.
Formed own ork in 1904 in
U.S. Ran orks for California
hotel chain. Had a hand in
west coast Schonberger
Bros' hit 'Whispering'. Got
in trouble for 'Avalon',
with Puccini's publishers,.
who claimed justly that chorus
was filched from their man's
work. Two other big hits:
'The Umbrella Man',
'Blueberry Hill'. Also ran:
'She's a New Kind of Old-
Fashioned Girl'.

JOE SANTLY
(1886-1962) Alley staffer/
cleffer doubling on vaude
boards. Hits: 'Tamiami Trail',
'Hawaiian Butterfly', and
'At the Moving Picture Ball'.

HARRY TIERNEY
(1895-1965) Irish-American
fully-schooled musician.
Staffer at London publishers
Francis, Day and Hunter
where wrote first songs
and a score for Andre Charlot,
famed revue producer. Back
in U.S. he joined Waterson,
Berlin and Snyder Co., wrote
for Ziegfeld Follies, had songs
interpolated into shows,
before writing complete
score for *Irene*. Ziegfeld
hired him to do score for
Rio Rita, another howling
success as play and film
(though no complete print
of movie — which starred
John Boles and Bebe Daniels
— survives). Also wrote
Beau Brummell, an operetta.
Hits: 'Castle of Dreams',
'Rio Rita', 'The Ranger's
Song', 'If You're In Love
You'll Waltz', 'Alice Blue
Gown'.

ALBERT VON TILZER
(1878-1956) A really ancient
Alleyman, dating from tear-
jerking ballad days. Started in
shoe trade. Real name Al
Gumm (Judy Garland a
relative). Elder brother
Harry, known as the 'Daddy
of Popular Song', wrote more
hits. Albert obeyed Harry's
rule: "Keep tunes to small
range so even a baby can
hum 'em": 'Take Me Out
To The Ball Game', 'Put Your
Arms Around Me Honey',
'I'll Be With You In Apple
Blossom Time'.

LEO TOWERS
(1901-73) Diminutive
cockney charmer with
bohemian touches. Wrote
'Sally' with Harry Leon and
had number of local hits
in thirties and forties, e.g.:
'A Street In Old Seville',
'When The Poppies Bloom
Again'.

HARRY WARREN
(1893-   ) King of the
Hollywood musical, but
so retiring that he's never
garnered the acclaim due
him. Son of Italian-
American bootmaker. Music
education as Catholic choir
boy. Carnival drummer,
film prop man, saloon
pianist before ringing bell
with first hit 'Rose Of The
Rio Grande', beloved of
jazz-age dance band
arrangers due to fill-in
holes in melody. In ms.
this sentence reads, "More
good-time novelties — 'I
Love My Baby', 'Home in
Pasadena' — before the call
west and a quiet life . . . ."
etc. Crafting movie songs,
particularly for the ever-
hungry dance director
Busby Berkeley. Sharing life
in the studio cubicle was
Swiss-born Al Dubin, Ally
warhourse hero of such
songs as 'Just A Girl That
Men Forget', 'The
Lonesomest Girl in Town'
and other cryers. Dubin the
wordsman arrived in movie-
town before Warren and had
hit with 'Tip-toe Through
The Tulips' and 'Painting
The Clouds With Sunshine'.
Together the shy Warren
and ebullient Dubin were
responsible for a mass of
movie hits: 'We're In The
Money', 'Shuffle Off to
Buffalo', 'You're Getting
To Be A Habit With Me',
'I Only Have Eyes For You',
'Lullaby Of Broadway'.

RICHARD WHITING
(1891-1938) Mild-mannered
composer of many deathless
tunes. Fairly well-educated,
started as manager of Remick
Music (Chicago) where he
wrote 'It's Tulip Time In
Holland','Mammy's Little
Coal Black Rose', 'And They
Called It Dixieland' and
'Till We Meet Again' (original
title 'Auf Wiedersehen').
'Japanese Sandman' continued
'Madam Butterfly' tradition
while 'Ain't We Got Fun'
gave the Jazz Age its slogan
(although World War I U.S.
troops had first coined the
phrase during battles in
Flanders Fields). Jazz Age
songs continued with
'Bimini Bay', 'Sleepy Time
Gal' and 'Ukulele Lady'.
Lured to Hollywood in
late twenties and remained
there till death by heart
attack. Among his talkie
hits: 'Louise', 'Beyond The
Blue Horizon', 'One Hour
With You', 'Hooray For
Hollywood' and 'Too
Marvelous For Words' (with
Johnny Mercer as lyricist).

HUGH WILLIAMS,
see WILL GROSZ

Discography

I'm Always Chasing Rainbows — Harry Fox (Columbia A-2557, New York, April 16th, 1918).

Alice Blue Gown — Edith Day (Victor 45176, Camden, New Jersey, February 2nd, 1920).

How Ya Gonna Keep 'Em Down On The Farm? — Joseph C. Smith's Orchestra (Victor 18533, New York, January 30th, 1919).

My Buddy — Henry Burr (Victor 18930, Camden, New Jersey, July 18th,1922).

Japanese Sandman — Paul Whiteman and his Ambassador Orchestra (Victor 18690, Camden, New Jersey, August 19th, 1920).

Dardanella — Ben Selvin's Novelty Orchestra (Victor 18633, New York, November 20th,1919).

Ain't We Got Fun — The Benson Orchestra of Chicago (Victor 18757, Camden, New Jersey, April 11th, 1921).

Bimini Bay — The Benson Orchestra of Chicago, directed by Roy Bargy (Victor 18824 and H.M.V. B-1309, Camden, New Jersey, September 28th, 1921).

Stumbling — Paul Whiteman and his Orchestra (Victor 18899, New York, March 30th,1922).

Dapper Dan — Jack Buchanan and the Trix Sisters (H.M.V. B-1302, Hayes, Middlesex, November 23rd, 1921).

Carolina In The Morning — Paul Whiteman and his Orchestra (Victor 18962 and H.M.V. B-1516, New York, September 21st, 1922).

Any Place Where I Make Money (Is Home Sweet Home To Me) — Irving and Jack Kaufman (Emerson Records 10594, New York, 1923).

She's A New Kind Of Old-Fashioned Girl — Jack Smith (Victor 21973, New York, April 24th, 1929).

My Blue Heaven — Gene Austin (Victor 20964, New York, September 14th, 1927).

Love Me Or Leave Me — Ruth Etting (Colombia 5553, Jan. 14, 1929).

Me And My Shadow — Jack Smith (Victor 20626, New York, April 28th, 1927). Accompanied by composer Dave Dreyer on piano.

I'll Get By — Ipana Troubadours, vocal Bing Crosby, (Columbia 1694-D, New York, December 28th, 1928).

It's A Sin To Tell A Lie — Ruth Etting (Rex 8853, London, August, 1936).

Dream Train — Nat Shilkret and the Victor Orchestra (Victor 21853, New York, January 17th, 1929).

Chloe — The Singing Sophomores, alias the Revellers (Columbia 1257-D, New York, November 29th, 1927).

Manhattan — Paul Whiteman and his Orchestra (Victor 19769, New York, September 1st, 1925).

Blue Moon — Al Bowlly (Victor 248489, New York, January 12th, 1935).

Parisian Pierrot — Noel Coward (H.M.V. B-8414, London, February 13th, 1936; original cast did not record this at the time of its first appearance in 1923).

Swanee — Al Jolson (Columbia A-2884, New York, January 9th, 1920).

At The Moving Picture Ball — Savoy Quartet (H.M.V. B-1154, Hayes, Middlesex, October 14th, 1920).

Charmaine — Guy Lombardo and his Royal Canadians (Columbia 1048-D, Chicago, June 13th, 1927).

You Were Meant For Me — Charles King (Victor 21965 and H.M.V. B-3070, Hollywood, April 11th, 1929).

Tip-toe Through The Tulips — Nick Lucas (Brunswick 4418, Los Angeles, May, 1929).

I Only Have Eyes For You — Eddy Duchin and his Orchestra (Victor 24665 and H.M.V. B-6551, Chicago, June 15th, 1934).

About A Quarter To Nine —Chick Bullock (Melotone M-13389, New York, April 9th, 1935).

Over The Rainbow — Judy Garland (Decca 2672, Los Angeles, July 18th, 1939).

Lady Of Spain — Ray Noble and the New Mayfair Dance Orchestra, vocal Al Bowlly (H.M.V. B-5999, London, March 24th, 1931).

The Farmyard Cabaret — Albert Whelan with Harry Hudson and his Melody Men (Panachord 25368-A, London, 1932). London, 1932).

Sally — Gracie Fields (H.M.V. B-3879, London, April 24th, 1931).

Red Sails In The Sunset — Al Bowlly (Victor 25142 and H.M.V. BD-295, New York, September 18th, 1935).

The Washing On The Siegried Line — Flanagan and Allen (Decca F-7297, London, September 27th, 1939).

When Day Is Done — Paul Whiteman and his Concert Orchestra (Victor 35828, New York, June 8th, 1927),

Roll Out The Barrel (The Beer Barrel Polka)—Will Glalie and his Orchestra (H.M.V. B-8910, Berlin, early 1939).

Lili Marlene — Lale Andersen (Electrola EG-6993, Berlin, C. August, 1939).

Biographies of songwriters

LEW BROWN
(1893-1958) Russian-born American producer/publisher as well as lyricist. Part of famous De Sylva, Brown and Henderson team, song and show writers of late twenties and early talkies. Bio filmed as *Best Things In Life Are Free*. Smash songs include: 'Don't Bring Lulu', 'Black Bottom', 'Sonny Boy', 'If I Had A Talking Picture Of You', 'Don't Sit Under The Apple Tree With Anyone Else But Me', 'Roll Out The Barrel'.

IRVING CAESAR
(1895-   ) Super song-salesman with such drive that only a bullet could stop him. In 1974 he's still demonstrating his hits to assemblies everywhere. Expert on Bernard Shaw. Author of best-selling children's safety songbook, music by Gerald ('All Of Me') Marks. Hits: 'I Want To Be Happy', 'Sometimes I'm Happy', 'Crazy Rhythm', 'Just A Gigolo', 'Animal Crackers in My Soup', 'Is It True What They Say About Dixie?', 'Swanee'.

STANLEY DAMERELL
(circa 1880-1951) Real name: Jack Stevens. Started in music hall as manager to star Arthur Roberts; later straight man to gormless comic Arthur Bass. Good stump speaker (especially outside shops) and lay preacher. Married my aunt. Was King Rat in Grand Order of Water Rats (whose ceremonial greeting was to drop the teeth). Hits: 'Let's All Sing Like The Birdies Sing', 'There's A Lovely Lake In Loveland', 'If', 'Unless', 'Faith', 'Fairy On The Clock', 'John Willie's Jazz Band'. Miss: 'The Organ Grinder Grinds All Day'.

AL DUBIN
(1891-1945) Swiss-born wordsman best known for his collaborations with Joe Burke and Harry Warren. Saw action with the artillery in World War I and used memories in 'Remember my Forgotten Man', 'Memories Of France' and 'My Dream Of The Big Parade'. Was on Billy Rose's payroll for some time, as was Lorenz Hart. A large man with a big heart and a talent for disappearances and sudden returns, with lyrics written on used enveolopes and menus. Hits include: 'Just A Girl That Men Forget', 'Painting The Clouds With Sunshine', 'Dancing With Tears In My Eyes', 'Shuffle Off To Buffalo', 'We're In The Money', 'You're Getting To Be A Habit With Me', 'Lullaby Of Broadway', 'Lulu's Back In Town', 'September In The Rain', 'Tip-toe Through The Tulips', 'I Only Have Eyes For You', 'About A Quarter To Nine'.

RAYMOND B' EGAN
(1890-1952) Canadian-born/ex-bank clerk. Voracious reader of magazine articles and romantic stories. Hits: 'And They Called It Dixieland', 'Till We Meet Again', 'Where The Morning Glories Grow', 'Sleepy Time Gal', 'Mammy's Little Coal Black Rose', 'Japanese Sandman', 'Ain't We Got Fun', 'Bimini Bay'.

ARTHUR FREED
(1894-1973) Real name: Arthur Grossman. Alley song plugger and vaude artist. Worked with Marx Bros, brushing up material for their vaude act. First big hit: 'I Cried For You'. Discovered by M.G.M.'s boy wonder Irving Thalberg, who taught him movie rudiments. Songs with Nacio Herb Brown for M.G.M. include: 'The Wedding Of The Painted Doll', 'Broadway Melody', 'Singin' In The Rain', 'Pagan Love Song', 'You Are My Lucky Star', 'You Were Meant For Me'. From 1939 he become producer and went on to be in charge of all MGM house musicals, including *Cabin in the Sky, Meet Me In St Louis, Easter Parade, Singin' In The Rain.*

BUD GREEN
(1897-   ) Austrian-born American Alley staffer. Wrote goodies with Sam Stept ('Do Something' for Helen Kane and 'There's A Tear For Every Smile In Hollywood' for early talkie). Also: 'Alabamy Bound', 'That's My Weakness Now', 'I'll Always Be In Love With You'.

E.Y. ('Yip') HARBURG
(1898-   ) Worked in electrical appliance trade till 1929. Words to revue songs. Later in Hollywood. Chief musical partners: Jay Gorney, Jerome Kern, Vernon Duke, Johnny Green, Harold Arlen. A sampling of his hits: 'Brother, Can You Spare A Dime?', 'It's Only A Paper Moon', 'April In Paris', 'What Wouldn't I Do For That Man?', 'Ding Dong The Witch Is Dead', 'How Are Things In Glocca Morra?', 'Old Devil Moon', 'I Could Go On Singing', 'Over The Rainbow'.

LORENZ HART
(1895-1943) Pint-sized major talent with good university background. Wrote Varsity shows at Columbia U. Met Richard Rodgers there. Translated German plays for Shubert Bros. Never an Alley worker. Film scores for Al Jolson, George M. Cohan and Jessie Matthews. See **RICHARD RODGERS** for partial list of hits.

HOWARD JOHNSON
(1887-1941) Alley staffer skilled at cornball comedy ditties and heart lyrics. Apparently not related to U.S. family restaurant chain. Goodies include: 'I Scream, You Scream, We All Scream For Ice Cream'. 'You'd Never Know That Old Home Town Of Mine', 'In The Woodshed She Said She Would' (early Gracie Fields record), 'M-O-T-H-E-R' (much parodied, best by Bing Crosby, George Burns and Jack Benny in forties pic), 'When The Moon Comes Over The Mountain' (large lady crooner Kate Smith's signature tune), 'At The Moving Picture Ball'.

GUS KAHN
(1886-1941) Very prolific wordsman, born in Germany. Married to fellow writer Grace Le Boy. Noted for deft wit and extraordinary ability to turn in clever switches on the old story. A few of his hits: 'Memories', 'I'll Say She Does', 'Pretty Baby', 'Side By Side', 'Toot, Toot, Tootsie, Goodbye', 'I'll See You In My Dreams', 'It Had To Be You', 'Yes, Sir, That's My Baby', 'Makin' Whoopee', 'Ukulele Lady', 'Dream A Little Dream Of Me', 'Carolina In The Morning', 'Ain't We Got Fun', 'Love Me Or Leave Me', 'Chloe'.

CLAY KEYES
(1892-1970) Real name: Henry Newbold. Liverpudlian who trod boards of variety as light comedian, known as smart dresser. Affected slight American accent: 'Oh Oh Oh I Wanna Go Home', 'The Handsome Gigolo'.

HARRY LEON
Real Name: Harry Sugarman. Ex-merchant navy seaman famous for his bent nose. Real London east-ender. Roving songwriter of Charing Cross Road/Denmark Street, fond of advances on royalties. During sixties he made living playing piano in pubs: 'Down Every Street' (as Art Noel), 'In A Golden Coach' (as Ronald Jameson), 'Sally'.

SAM M. LEWIS
(1885-1959) Arch Alleyman who usually wrote with Joe Young. Glut of hits during Great War. 'Where Did Robinson Crusoe Go With Friday On Saturday Night?', 'Hello Central, Give Me No-Man's Land', 'Rockabye Your Baby With A Dixie Melody', 'My Mammy', 'Dinah', 'Five Foot Two, Eyes Of Blue', 'I'm Sitting On Top Of The World'. All of these were written with **JOE YOUNG** (1889-1939), who also wrote 'Yaaka Hula Hicky Dula' and 'I'm Gonna Sit Right Down And Write Myself A Letter' without his partner.

JOSEPH McCARTHY
(1885-1943) Cafe singer, Alley staffer who rose to Broadway musical comedy *(Irene, Kid Boots, Rio Rita)*. Hits: 'You Made Me Love You', 'They Go Wild, Simply Wild, Over Me', 'What Do You Want To Make Those Eyes At Me For?', 'I Miss You Most Of All', 'Rio Rita', 'The Ranger's Song', 'Following The Sun Around', 'If You're In Love You'll Waltz', 'I'm Always Chasing Rainbows'.

LEW POLLACK
(1895-1946) Boy soprano, then vaude singer/pianist. Later Hollywood. Hits: 'Diane', 'At The Codfish Ball', 'Miss Annabelle Lee', 'That's A Plenty', 'In The Middle Of A Kiss', 'Charmaine'.

BILLY ROSE
(1899-1966) Real name: Rosenberg. Legendary Broadway showman. Wrote stage scores, produced outdoor spectacles, ran Diamond Horseshoe night club in New York, had syndicated column, lived long enough to condemn rock 'n' roll. Hits include: 'That Old Gang Of Mine', 'Does The Spearmint Lose Its Flavor On The Bedpost Overnight?', 'Don't Bring Lulu', 'It Happened In Monterey', 'Happy Days And Lonely Nights', 'It's Only A Paper Moon', 'Me And My Shadow'.

WILLIAM TRACEY
(1893-1957) Irish-American minor wordsmith of clerkly appearance (affected steel frame glasses). Employed as oddbody staffer at Alley firm. Adept at adding words to finished tunes: 'Gee, But It's Great To Meet A Friend From Your Home Town' (quintessential close harmony vaude song), 'Mammy O' Mine' (Sophie Tucker specialty).

ROY TURK
(1892-1934) Special material writer for Nora Bayes and Sophie Tucker. Later in Hollywood. Hits: 'Gimme A Little Kiss, Will Ya Huh?', 'Walkin' My Baby Back Home', 'Where The Blue Of The Night Meets The Gold Of The Day', 'Mean To Me', 'Are You Lonesome Tonight?', 'I'll Get By'.

GEORGE WHITING
(1884-1943) Classy, dapper cafe and cabaret singer and song delineator. Also vaude-ville. Wrote 'My Blue Heaven', also 'My Wife's Gone To The Country', with Irving Berlin, and Prohibition era song 'Saloon', with Ernest ('When Irish Eyes Are Smiling') Ball.

JOE YOUNG (see SAM M. LEWIS).

Further reading
and Acknowledgments

Books about popular music before rock 'n' roll are, on the whole, better researched and better written than rock books. They reflect a more leisurely way of life, a more logical way of thinking, a less venomous way of feeling and reacting. And (even though song writer Edgar Leslie wasn't bothered by Shakespeare) the Alleymen read newspapers, magazines, light verse and even books. Rock mostly revels in the visual and tactile rather than the written word.

Because there was no book that told the story of pop music from ragtime to rock I spent three years writing one which was eventually called *After the Ball* (Allen Lane, 1973). It's a painless read, stuffed with facts and theories — sweetened with jokes and apocryphal stories. I read an inordinate amount of books during my research for *Ball* (such as the works of C.E.M. Joad and most jazz books). I found the most rewarding material in magazines, newspapers, trade papers and record bags of the period. But there were a few books which I found myself constantly referring to, and though I have a certain reluctance in revealing my trick sources, here they are:

Henry Pleasant's *Serious Music — And All That Jazz* (Gollancz, London, 1969). A breath-taking bird's-eye-view of the decline of European music and the rise of Afro-American as the new serious music.

Isaac Goldberg, *Tin Pan Alley* (John Day, New York, 1930). Now out of print. Subtitled "A Chronicle of the American Popular Music Racket", this is the first examination of pop as an art and an industry. Quite brilliant. Deals fearlessly with the black and the Jewish elements in pop.

Neil Leonard, *Jazz and the White Americans* (University of Chicago Press, Chicago, 1962). Subtitled "The Acceptance of a New Art Form." A very erudite and militant thesis. How the white establishment castrated jazz. Nevertheless it's stimulating.

Hazel Meyer, *The Gold in Tin Pan Alley* (Lippincott, Philadelphia, 1958). Semi-historical inside dope on Alley wheeling and dealing. Tricky technical stuff well described.

Marshall and Jean Stearns, *Jazz Dance — The Story of American Vernacular Dance* (Macmillan, New York, 1968). Worth digging in this trove for facts about the ragtime animal dancing and Charlestoning and where it all came from. Rather hard on white dancers, and nothing about the Lancashire clog. Even so, epic.

Alec Wilder, *American Popular Song — the Great Innovators (1900-1950)* edited by James Maher, (Oxford University Press, London, 1972). For the first time in book form, pop songs are musically analysed and we see the cunning, the artistry and the cliché.Wilder, a hit composer himself, proves that the micro-art has its sublime moments and can rest on the same cloud as Beethoven and Bach. A trifle inexperienced Alley-wise (the first time Wilder ever heard "Bill Bailey" was when he was researching his book!)

Nat Shapiro, editor, *Popular Music — an Annotated Index* (Adrian Press, New York, 1964). These five volumes list writers, publishers, popularizers and dates of hit songs between 1920 and 1964, plus introductory notes on each decade or era. Unlike *Variety's* cavalcade of popular music hits, the Shapiro books include blues and country records as far back as the twenties, thus avoiding that familiar old show-biz scholar's habit of ignoring the blacks and the hillbillies and raving on about Berlin-Kern-Gershwin-Rodgers-Hart-Porter (who, good as they were, are by no means the beginning and end of pop music, as I hope this song book has shown).

I would like to thank the following for their unstinting help in the preparation of this book: Pat Howgill and Ron White of EMI Music Publishing, Oliver Caldecott and Annabel Whittet (my editors at Wildwood House), Chris Ellis of EMI, Walter Wager of ASCAP, James Maher, Harry Warren, Bud Green, Edgar Leslie, Mrs Richard Whiting, Donald Kahn, Nick Lucas, Irving Caesar, Dr Neil Daniels, Abe Olman, Jimmy Phillips of Peter Maurice Music, Tolchard Evans, John Kobal, The Performing Rights Society, Bert Jones of Francis, Day & Hunter, Fiachra Trench, Jimmy Kennedy, Anne and Charles Sprawson, Brian Rust and Sam Coslow. Also, of course, my mother for again allowing me to monopolize her dining room.